Golden Lilies

Originally published as
MY LADY OF THE
CHINESE COURTYARD
translated by
Elizabeth Cooper

A d a p t e d

a n d   w i t h   a

f o r e w o r d

b y

E I L E E N

G O U D G E

I l l u s t r a t e d   b y
Z h a n g   Q i n g

Kwei - li

GOLDEN LILIES

A John Curtis Book
Hodder & Stoughton
LONDON SYDNEY AUCKLAND TORONTO

British Library Cataloguing in Publication Data

Kwei-Li
  Golden lilies.
  1. China. Social life, history
  I. Title   II. Goudge, Eileen
  951

  ISBN 0-340-53622-5

First published in Great Britain 1991

This work is based on My Lady of the Chinese
Courtyard by Elizabeth Cooper, published in 1914
by Frederick A. Stokes Company.

Reproduced by arrangement with Viking Penguin Inc.

Designed by Joy Chu.

Published by Hodder and Stoughton,
a division of Hodder and Stoughton Ltd,
Mill Road, Dunton Green, Sevenoaks, Kent TN13 2YA
Editorial Office: 47 Bedford Square, London WC1B 3DP

Printed in Great Britain by St Edmundsbury Press Ltd,
Bury St Edmunds, Suffolk

For every pair of golden lilies
there is a *kang* of tears.

—*Old Chinese saying*

Acknowledgments

In the hundred years or so since these letters were written, the term "labor of love" has become a cliché. But this adaptation has been just that. The following people contributed not only their time and considerable talents, but a rare enthusiasm inspired by the poetry of Kwei-li's voice, and the unique view she provides of a vanished China.

First, and foremost, my invaluable assistant, Catherine Jacobes, whose intrepid search for a Chinese illustrator sent her from the cloisters of academia to the labyrinths of New York's Chinatown. From a tiny frame shop on Baxter Street to an old-age home where only a few even spoke English, her quest eventually led to Zhang Qing. I thank her also for the many hours she has spent researching the book's provenance, and for finding sinologists to help. She is the true godmother of *Golden Lilies*.

Zhang Qing, whose exquisite illustrations are the "eyes" to Kwei-li's voice.

Diane Chang, who translated for her brother, Qing, and assisted him in creating his illustrations. With her gentle diplomacy in negotiating his contract, she also served to remind us that the spirit of Kwei-li lives on in modern China.

Kay Hechler, at Viking, who loved the book enough to send it to her mother.

Rita Mao Hechler, known to millions as "He Li-Da," China's "Voice of America," who generously gave of her valuable time and expertise in researching information about Kwei-li's family.

Dr. Chi Wang, of the Library of Congress, who was kind enough to assist Mrs. Hechler in her research, and who provided corrections in the original translation, as well as English meanings of some hitherto untranslated Chinese words and expressions.

Ling Yun Ji and Kuang-fu Chu of the New York Public Library, Oriental Division.

Pamela Dorman, my editor at Viking, for her thoughtful guidance.

Neil Stuart, for his eye for beauty.

Elaine Koster, who inspired my search to rediscover a book I had once loved.

My husband and agent, Albert Zuckerman of Writers House, for his love and support.

I first happened upon Kwei-li's story ten years ago while researching Chinese customs for a novel I was writing. At the local library in Santa Cruz, California, among the dusty stacks of biographical works, a timeworn volume caught my eye. It was called *My Lady of the Chinese Courtyard*. More than half a century old, its cover discolored, its pages jaundiced with age, it looked as if no one had read it in years. I had never heard of its author, Elizabeth Cooper, or its long-defunct publisher. Opening its musty pages, I sneezed. Okay, I thought, nothing to get excited about. I was wrong.

Years later, its first words would still haunt me: "The house on the mountaintop has lost its soul."

Here was treasure: a hidden door into an inner courtyard of old China.

I was transported back a hundred years, to the home of a wealthy Chinese nobleman in Soochow, where his young bride is pining for her absent husband. She is Kwei-li, the highborn daughter of a viceroy of Chih-li, and accomplished as well as beautiful. Educated even, we are told—unusual in an era when less than ten percent of Chinese women could read or write.

She is also a woman in love—with a husband she had never once seen until their wedding ceremony. Of that occasion, she recalls: "Do you remember when first you raised my veil and looked long into my eyes? I was thinking, 'Will he find me beautiful?' and in fear I could look but a moment . . . But in that moment I saw that you were tall and beautiful, that your skin was clear and your teeth like pearls."

I was Kwei-li's age, eighteen, when I first married. Reading of Kwei-li's struggle to learn the ways of her new husband's family, which according to Chinese custom she was bound to honor and obey over her own, I could feel for her. And as a new bride, she also has to cope with a bossy mother-in-law, family squabbles, a big kitchen, and servants. Then, while her husband is on an extended overseas diplomatic mission, she discovers that she is pregnant with her first child!

My firstborn, Michael, nearly died in his first moments of life, and he was sickly for some weeks after. I recall clearly those anxious days, peering into his incubator. I remember aching to hold him, and yet, superstitiously, I feared that if I made that connection, if I dared to love him more than I already did, he would be snatched from me.

My son survived; Kwei-li was not so lucky. Her cherished baby boy, whose ear she had pierced in order to trick the gods into thinking he was a girl (and thus unworthy of being claimed by them), didn't live long enough for his father to see or hold him. Her faith shattered, Kwei-li fell into despair. Her anxious family found an abandoned baby girl on a nearby towpath, and placed her in Kwei-li's arms. Of this she tells us: ". . . I sat stiff and still, and tried to push away the little body pressing close against me; but at the touch of baby mouth and fingers, springs that were dead seemed stirring in my heart again."

Halfway through this remarkable epistle, I felt as if I had known Kwei-li all my life. Though separated by a century and a vast cultural gulf, we weren't really so different, she and I. Hers is the story of wives and mothers everywhere; of joy and despair, of promises and compromises, of the grains of domestic life that fill Kwei-li's "rice bowl" to overflowing. Under her rooftree we are joined, East and West, by the common landscape of our experience.

The tale of Kwei-li, as a young bride, ends with the imminent return of her beloved husband. The second group of letters, dated twenty-five years later, is addressed to her mother-in-law, to whom she has grown devoted. Kwei-li, by now, is a mother many times over. She is also a woman of prominence. Her husband is governor of Kiang-su under the new revolutionary government of President Yuan Shih-kai, who dethroned the last Ching emperor, Pu-yi. It is 1912, a time of chaotic change for China.

Kwei-li, living far from her family's ancestral home, feels displaced and unsettled not only by the loss of familiar surroundings but by the onset of modern times. A daughter with unbound feet who wishes to become a doctor! A son, educated abroad, who openly defies the government! Yet she wisely keeps her perspective, focusing on what is most important to her: her children. In the last letter, she speaks of cradling her first grandchild in her arms: ". . . I have learned in life's great, bitter school that the joy of my Chinese womanhood is to stand within the sheltered courtyard, with my family close about me, and my son's son in my arms."

Still, I was curious to learn more about Kwei-li's history, so I decided to do some research. I learned that she was, most likely, born in 1867, and married in 1885. Her first son was born a year later—and the fever to which he succumbs was, I believe, typhus, which was then ravaging China.

By the time Kwei-li's husband became governor of Kiang-su, China had seen the bloody Boxer Rebellion of 1900, the death of the dowager Empress Kuang-hsu, and the toppling of the Imperial throne. Kwei-li witnesses with veiled displeasure the influx of foreigners into her native country—and their "unladylike" wives. Occasionally she finds her own modern daughters rude and unladylike as well. She watches as her son's bride is borne to the altar, not in a sedan chair, but in a motorcar adorned with satin rosettes. Later, she agonizes when that son, Ting-fang, is accused of being involved in an assassination attempt against a high government official and sentenced to death.

Luckily, Ting-fang did not die a traitor. My research revealed a Dr. Ting-fang Liu who lived at that time and who became a distinguished professor and theologian. Born in 1891, he was educated in Shanghai, and later at Columbia University, where he earned his doctorate. After receiving a divinity degree from Yale, he became the first Chinese ever appointed to teach any subject other than Chinese at Union Theological Seminary. After returning to China, Dr. Ting-fang Liu, among other achievements, was elected Dean of the School of Theology at Yenching University. He is listed in the *Directory of Contemporary Chinese Who's Who*, published in Japan in 1937.

Of Kwei-li, far less is traceable. Our best source remains Elizabeth Cooper:

> I knew her many years afterward—her husband having been ap-
> pointed governor of Kiang-su—when she was the happy mother
> of sons and daughters. She was a blessing to our province in
> many ways. Homes for the poor were erected, schools for girls
> were started, and the generous hands of Kwei-li were ever open
> to her people. Although in the many charities that were started
> in the provincial capital her name was never mentioned, yet we
> who knew realized that it was the wife of the governor who was
> the power behind the throne . . .

Ten years after I had first read Cooper's little book—during
which time I had raised a family and written books of my own—I
was reminded of her by the chance remark of a publisher who mentioned she was looking for a book about life in China. I immediately
thought of Kwei-li. By then, however, I'd forgotten both the book's
title and the author's name. So it seemed a bit like searching for a
needle in a haystack. After numerous frustrating phone calls (includ-
ing several from my home in New York to Santa Cruz, where a
gem of a librarian came up with a directory for partial title listings),
I located a single, crumbling copy of *My Lady of the Chinese Courtyard*
in the depths of the Brooklyn Public Library. Rereading these letters after a decade, I found them as fresh and enchanting as I did
the first time.

I have retitled the book *Golden Lilies*, as a reminder of Kwei-li's
bound feet, a symbol of old China's women. Kwei-li, like all well-
born girls of her time (as well as many peasant girls), had had her

feet bound—toes curled under, and the arch broken—from her fifth birthday to achieve the goal of three-inch feet, which would nestle in the bowl of a teacup. These "golden lilies" were greatly prized as objects of supreme beauty, as well as erotic stimuli. The prevailing myth was that bound feet made women not only more desirable wives but better lovers.

The changes I made in the text itself were minimal. I have modernized "thee" and "thou" to "you," and rearranged some of the archaic syntax for clarity. But otherwise, I have faithfully followed Elizabeth Cooper's text, which she refers to in her preface as a "translation" of Kwei-li's original letters, given to her by Kwei-li's husband. It is not clear what liberties Mrs. Cooper may have taken in embellishing these letters with her own research and observations, based on her ten years as the wife of an American missionary in Shanghai. To my knowledge, Kwei-li's own letters—if they existed at all—have never been recovered. We do know that epistolary "memoirs" purporting to be fact were quite common among late-eighteenth-century and early-nineteenth-century missionary writers. I feel, however, that it is likely that Kwei-li *did* exist, and that Elizabeth Cooper knew her. Certainly Ting-fang Liu's existence is a matter of record, and though the accuracy of some of the biographical details Elizabeth Cooper provides is subject to scholarly dispute, it seems highly probable that he was, indeed, Kwei-li's son.

Pamela Dorman, my editor at Viking, and I both felt that illustrations would enhance the text—particularly Kwei-li's haunting descriptions of places and traditions unknown to most of us. Our search led us to Zhang Qing, one of a handful of modern Chinese artists who still paint in the traditional Chinese style. Born in Shanghai in 1944, he studied Chinese painting at the School of Art and Design in Shanghai, where he was influenced by such traditional techniques as third-century stone-carving and Ming Dynasty woodcuts. His paintings and murals depicting Chinese life have brought him renown in his native country, as well as a growing reputation in the United States, where he is presently a visiting professor at the City University of New York. Many of his illustrations for *Golden Lilies* are drawn from his own memories of Soochow, as well as from his grandmother's ancestral home.

Last, I must pay tribute to Kwei-li herself. I am convinced that, somehow, she was shining a guiding light on my efforts. And that she truly meant it when she wrote, quoting Confucius: "Birth is not a beginning, nor death an end."

I hope you will feel, as I do, that Kwei-li has indeed found a permanent place in our minds and hearts.

Eileen Goudge
March 1990

Part One

My Dear One,

The house on the mountaintop has lost its soul. It is nothing but a palace with empty windows. I go upon the terrace and look over the valley where the sun sinks a golden red ball, casting long purple shadows on the plain. Then I remember that you are not coming from the city to me, and I say to myself that there can be no dawn that I can see, and no sunset to gladden my eyes, unless I share it with you.

But do not think that I am unhappy. I do everything the same as if you were here, and in everything I say, "Would this please my Master?" Meh-ki wished to put your long chair away, as she said it was too big; but I did not permit it. It must rest where I can look at it and imagine I see you lying in it, smoking your water pipe; and

1

the small table is always nearby, where you can reach out your hand for your papers and the drink you love. Meh-ki also brought out the dwarf pine tree and put it on the terrace, but I remembered you said it looked like an old man who had been beaten in his childhood, and I gave it to her for one of the inner courtyards. She thinks it very beautiful, and so I did once; but I have learned to see with your eyes, and I know that a tree made straight and beautiful and tall by the gods is more to be regarded than one that has been bent and twisted by man.

Such a long letter I am writing you. I am so glad that you made me promise to write you every seventh day, and to tell you all that passes within my household and my heart. Your Honorable Mother says it is not seemly to send communication from my hand to yours. She says it was a thing unheard of in her girlhood, and that we younger generations have passed the limits of all modesty and womanliness. She wishes me to have the writer or your brother send you the news of your household; but that I will not permit. It must come from me, your wife. Each one of these

strokes will come to you bearing my message. You will not tear the covering roughly as you did those great official letters; nor will you crush the papers quickly in your hand, because it is the written word of Kwei-li, who sends with each stroke of her brush a part of her heart.

My Dear One,

My first letter to you was full of sadness and longing because you were newly gone from me. Now a week has passed, the sadness is still in my heart, but it is buried deep for only me to know. I have my duties that must be done, my daily tasks that only I can do since your Honorable Mother handed me the keys to the rice bin. I realize the great honor she does me, and that at last she trusts me and believes me no child as she did when I first entered her household.

Can I ever forget that day when I first came to my husband's people? I had the one great consolation of a bride, my parents had not sent me away empty-handed. The procession was almost a *li* [half mile] in length, and I watched with a swelling heart the many tens of coolies carrying my household goods. There were silken coverlets for the beds, and they were folded to show their richness and carried on red lacquered tables of great value. There were the household utensils of many kinds, the vegetable dishes, the baskets, the camphor wood baskets containing my clothing, tens upon tens of them; and I said within my heart as they passed me by, "Enter my new home before me. Help me to find a loving welcome." Then at the end of the chanting procession I came in my red chair of marriage, so closely covered I could barely breathe. My trembling feet could scarce support me as they helped me from the chair, and my hand shook with fear as I was being led into my new household. She stood bravely before you, that little girl dressed in red and gold, her hair twined with pearls and jade, her arms heavy with bracelets and with rings on each tiny finger, but with all her bravery she was frightened—frightened. She was away from her parents for the first time, away from all who loved her, and she knew if she did not meet with approval in her new home her rice bowl would be full of bitterness for many moons to come.

After the obeisance to the ancestral tablet and after we had fallen upon our knees before your Honorable Parent, I then saw for the first time the face of my husband. Do you remember when first you raised my veil and looked long into my eyes? I was thinking, "Will he find me beautiful?" and in fear I could look but for a moment, then my eyes fell and I would not raise them to yours again. But in that moment I saw that you were tall and beautiful, that your skin was clear and your teeth like pearls. I was secretly glad within my heart, because I have known of brides who, when they saw their husbands for the first time, wished to scream in terror, as they were old and ugly. I thought to myself that I could be happy with this tall, strong young man if I found favor in his sight, and I said a little prayer to Kwan-yin. Because she has answered that prayer, each day I place a candle at her feet to show my gratitude.

I think your Honorable Mother has passed me the keys of the

household to take my mind from my loss. She says that a heart that
is busy cannot mourn, and my days are full of duties. I arise in the
morning early, and after seeing that my hair is tidy, I take a cup of
tea to the Aged One and make my obeisance; then I place the rice
and water in their dishes before the God of the Kitchen, and light a
tiny stick of incense for his altar, so that our day may begin auspi-
ciously. After the morning meal I consult with the cook and steward. The vegetables must be checked carefully and the fish
inspected, and I must ask the price that has been paid, because
often a hireling is hurried and forgets that a bargain is not made
with a breath.

I carry the great keys and feel much pride when I open the door
of the storeroom. Why, I do not know, unless it is because of the

realization that I am the head of this large household. If the servants or their children are ill, they come to me instead of to your Honorable Mother, as in former times. I settle all difficulties, unless they are too rare or heavy for one of my mind and experience.

Then I go with the gardener to the terrace and help him arrange the flowers for the day. I love the stone-flagged terrace, with its low marble balustrade, resting close against the mountain to which it seems to cling.

I always stop a moment and look over the valley, because it was from here I watched you when you went to the city in the morning and here I waited your return. Because of my love for it and the rope of remembrance with which it binds me, I keep it beautiful with rugs and flowers.

It speaks to me of happiness and brings back memories of summer days spent idling in a quiet so still that we could hear the rustle of the bamboo grasses on the hillside down below; or, still more dear, the evenings passed close by your side, watching the lingering moon's soft touch, which brightened each door and archway into jade as it passed.

I long for you, I love you, I am yours.

Your Wife

My Dear One,

The hours of one day are as like each other as are twin blossoms from the pear tree. There is no news to tell you. The mornings are passed in the duties that come to all women who have the care of a household, and in the afternoons I am on the terrace with your sister. But first of all, your August Mother must be made comfortable for her sleep, and then the peace is indeed wonderful.

Mah-li and I take our embroidery and sit upon the terrace, where we pass long hours watching the people in the valley below. The faint blue smoke curls from a thousand dwellings, and we try to imagine the lives of those who dwell beneath the rooftrees. We see the peasants in their rice fields; watch them dragging the rich mud from the bottoms of the canal for fertilizing; hear the shrill whistle of the duck man as, with long bamboo, he drives the great flock of ducks homeward or sends them over the fields to search for insects. We see the wedding procession far below, and can but faintly follow the great covered chair of the bride and the train of servants carrying the possessions to the new home. Often the wailing of the mourners in a funeral comes to our ears, and we lean far over the balcony to watch the coolies scatter the spirit money that will pay the dead man's way to the land of the gods. But yesterday we saw the procession carrying the merchant Wong to his resting place of the dead. There were many thousands of *cycee* spent upon his funeral. Your brother tells me his sons made great boast that no man has been buried with such pomp in all the province. But it only brings more clearly the remembrance that he began this life a sampan coolie and ended it with many millions. But his millions did not bring him happiness. He labored without ceasing, and then, without living to enjoy the fruit, worn out, departed, one knows not where.

Yesterday we heard the clang-clang of a gong and saw the *Taotai* [magistrate] pass by, his men carrying the boards and banners with his official rank and virtues written upon them, and we counted the red umbrellas and wondered if some poor peasant was in deep trouble.

It is beautiful here now. The hillside is purple with the autumn bloom and the air is filled with a golden haze. The red leaves drift slowly down the canal and tell me that soon the winter winds will come. Outside the walls the insects sing sleepily in the grass, seeming to know that their southward flight carries my thoughts to you. All is sad, and sad as the clouded moon my longing face, and my eyes are filled with tears. Not at twilight nor at gray of dawn can I find happiness without you, my lord, mine own, and "endless are the days as trailing creepers."

Your Wife

My Dear One,

I have much to tell you. My last letter was unhappy, and these little slips of paper must bring you joy, not sorrow, else why the written word?

First, I must tell you that your brother Chih-peh will soon be married. You know he has long been betrothed to Li-ti, the daughter of the Governor of Chih-li, and soon the bride will be here. We have been arranging her apartments. We do not know how many home servants she will bring, and we are praying the gods to grant her discretion, because with servants from a different province there are sure to be jealousies and the retelling of small tales that disturb the harmony of a household.

Many tales have been brought us of her great beauty, and we hear she has much education. Your August Mother is much disturbed over the latter, for as she says—and justly too—overlearning is not good for women. It is not meet to give them books in which to store their embroidery silks. But I—I am secretly delighted, and Mah-li, your sister, is transported with joy. I think, within our hearts, although we would not even whisper it to the night wind, we are glad that there will be three instead of two to bear the burden of the discourses of your Honorable Mother. Not that she talks too much, you understand, nor that her speech is not stored full of wisdom, but—she talks—and we must listen.

We have other news. A new slave girl has come into our household. As you know, there has been a great famine to the north of

us, and the boats, who follow all disaster, full of hungry people,
have been anchored in our canal. I do not know why the August
One desired to add one more to take of rice beneath our rooftree;
but she is here. Ho-tai was brought before me, a little peasant girl,
dressed in faded blue trousers and a jacket that had been many
times to the washing pool. Her black hair was coiled in the girlhood
knot at the side of the head, and in it she had stuck a pumpkin blossom. She was such a pretty little country flower, and looked so
helpless, I drew her to me and questioned her. She told me there
were many within their compound wall: grandmother, father,
mother, brothers, sisters, uncles, and cousins. The rice was gone,
the heavy clothing and everything of value in the pawnshop. Death
was all around them, and they watched each day as he drew
nearer—nearer. Then came the buyers of girls. They had money
that would buy rice for the winter and mean life to all. But the
mother would not listen. She was told over and over that the price
of one would save the many. But she would not sell her daughter.
Her nights were spent in weeping and her days in fearful watching.
At last, worn out, despairing, she went to a far-off temple to ask
Kwan-yin, the Mother of Mercies, for help in her great trouble.
While she was gone, Ho-tai was taken to the women in the boat at
the water gate, and many pieces of silver were paid the father.
When the stomach is empty, pride is not strong, and there were
many small bodies crying for rice that could only be bought with the
sacrifice of one. That night, as they started down the canal, they
saw on the towpath a peasant woman, her dress open far below her
throat, her hair loose and flying, her eyes swollen and dry from over-
weeping, moaning pitifully, stumbling on in the darkness, searching
for the boat that had anchored at the water gate; but it was gone.
Poor little Ho-tai! She said, "It was my mother!" and as she told

me, her face was wet with the bitter rain. I soothed her and told her
we would make her happy, and I made a little vow in my heart that
I would find that mother and bring peace to her heart again.

The summer wanes and the autumn is upon us with all its mists
and shadows of purple and gray. The camphor trees look from the
distance like great balls of fire, and the eucalyptus tree, in its dress
of brilliant yellow, is a gaily painted court lady. If one short glimpse
of you could gladden my heart, then all my soul would be filled with
the beauty of this time, these days of red and gold. But now I seek
you the long night through, and turn to make my arm your pillow —
but you are gone.

I am your wife who longs for you.   *15*

My Dear One,

We have a daughter-in-law. Not only have we a daughter-in-law, but we have servants and household furnishings and clothing—and clothing—and clothing. I am sure that if her gowns could be laid side by side, they would reach around the world. She is as fair as the spring blossoms, and of as little use. An army encamped upon us could not have so upset our household as the advent of this one maiden. She brought with her rugs to cover the floors, embroideries and hangings for the walls, scrolls and sayings of Confucius and Mecius to hang over the seats of honor—to show us that she is an admirer of the classics—screens for the doorways, even a huge bed all carved and gilded and with hangings and tassels of gay silk.

Your Honorable Mother, after viewing the goods piled in the courtyards, called her bearers and told us she was taking tea with a friend in the village of Sung-dong. I think she chose this friend because she lives the farthest from our compound walls. I alone was left to direct the placing of this furniture. Li-ti was like a butterfly, flitting hither and thither, doing nothing, talking much. The bed must be placed so that the Spirits of Evil passing over it in the nighttime could not take the souls of the sleepers away with them. The screens must stand at the proper angle guarding the doorways from the spirits who, in their straight, swift flight through the air, fall against these screens instead of entering the house. She gravely explained to me that the souls who dwell in the darkness like to take up their abode in newly organized households, and many precautions must be made against them. She even seriously considered the roof, to see if all the points curved upward, so that the spirits lighting upon them would be carried high above the open courtyards. I do not know what would have happened to your ancestral rooftree if it had not met with her approval. I was many heartsful glad that your August Mother was taking tea in a far-off village, as Li-ti even wanted to install a new god in the kitchen. This I would not permit. Can you imagine your Mother's face if a god from a stranger family was in the niche above the kitchen stove? Happily all was over when your Honorable Mother returned. She is not pleased with this, her newest, daughter-in-law, and she talks—and talks—and talks. She says the days will pass most slowly until she sees the father of Li-ti. She yearns to tell him that a man knows how to spend a million pieces of money in marrying off his daughter, but knows not about how to spend a hundred thousand in bringing up his child. If this great Governor of Chih-li has much wisdom, he will stay long within his province. I have just heard for the hundredth time the saying of Confucius, "Birth is not a beginning, nor is death an end." In my despair I said deep down within my breast, "I am sure it will not be an end for you, O Mother-in-law. You will go to the River of Souls talking, talking, always talking—but the gods will be good to me. You must pass before me, and I will not hasten so as to overtake you on the way." I beg your pardon, dear one. I lack respect to your Most Honorable Parent, but my soul is sore and tried and I can find no quiet.

> I am,
> Your Wife

6

My Dear One,

"The five worst infirmities that afflict the female are indocility, discontent, slander, jealousy, and silliness. The worst of them all, and the parent of the other four, is silliness." Does that not sound familiar to your ears? Life is serious here in your ancestral home since we have taken to ourselves a daughter-in-law. The written word for the trouble is two women beneath one rooftree, and I greatly fear that the wise man who invented writing had knowledge that cost him dear. Perhaps he, too, had a daughter-in-law.

Yet, with it all, Li-ti is such a child. Ah, I see you smile. You say she is only three years less in age than I; yet, you see, I have had the honor of living a year by the side of your Most August Mother and have acquired much knowledge from the very fountain-head of wisdom. Perchance Li-ti also will become a sage—if she be not gathered to her ancestors before her allotted time, which depends upon the strength of body and of mind that they may have willed her.

To me, she is the light of this old palace. She is the true spirit of laughter, and, "When the happy laugh, the gods rejoice." She is continually in disgrace with your Honorable Mother, and now the Elder One has decided that both she and Mah-li, your sister, shall learn a text from the sage Confucius each day for penance. They are now in the inner courtyard, studying the six shadows that attend the six virtues. I can hear them saying over and over to each other, "Love of goodness without the will to learn casts the shadow called

foolishness"—now a laugh—then again they begin, "Love of knowledge without the will to learn casts the shadow called instability"—
giggling and much talking. I am afraid they will never arrive at the
shadow cast by the love of truth, and after I have written you I will
go in and help them, that they may not be reprimanded.

Li-ti takes her duties more seriously now, these same duties con-
sisting of dressing for the day. In the morning she seats herself before her mirror, and two maids attend her, one to hold the great
brass bowl of water, the other to hand her the implements of the
toilet. While the face is warm she covers it with honey mixed with
perfume, and applies the rice powder until her face is as white as

the rice itself. The cheeks are rouged, the touch of red is placed
upon the lower lip, the eyebrows are shaped like the true willow
leaf, and the hair is dressed. Her hair is wonderful (but I say within
my heart, not as long or as thick as mine), and she adorns it with
many jewels of jade and pearls. Over her soft clothing of fine linen
she draws the rich embroidered robes of silk and satin. Then her
jewels, earrings, beads, bracelets, rings, the tiny mirror in the embroidered case, the bag with its rouge and powder fastened to her
side by long red tassels. When all things are in place, she rises a
being glorified, a thing of beauty from her glossy hair to the toe of
her tiny embroidered shoe. I watch her with a little envy, because
when you were here I did the same. Now that my husband is away,
it is not meet that I make myself too seemly for other eyes. The
rouge brush and the powder have not been near my face, and I
have searched my clothing chests to find gowns fitting for a woman
who is alone.

Your Mother says poor Li-ti is too vain, and repeats to her the
saying, "More precious in a woman is a virtuous heart than a face
of beauty." But I say she is our butterfly, she brings the joys of
summer. One must not expect a lace handkerchief to hold tears, and
she fulfills her woman's destiny. Chih-peh, your brother, is inexpressibly happy. He adores his pretty blossom. He follows her with eyes
that worship, and when she is in disgrace with your August Mother,
he is desolate. When needs be she is sent to her apartment, until the
Honorable One has retired from sight, then he hurriedly goes to his
beloved. Soon I hear them laughing gaily, and know the storm is
over.

The rains have come and we cannot pass long days upon the terrace. The whole valley is shrouded in gray mists, and the peasants
have gone from the fields. The path down the mountainside is

empty, except for the men with the great umbrella hats and capes of straw, bringing the vegetables to the monastery below. The old abbot of the monastery is in great trouble. Some men have come and wish to erect long poles with wires on them. It is feared it will interrupt the *feng-shiu* [harmony] of the temple. The good spirits of the air cannot pass, and will rest upon these ugly poles instead of coming to the temple rooftree. The abbot has wailed and gone to the magistrate; but he will not interfere, as the men have many tens of thousands of *cycee* and quite likely will work their will.

Such foolish letters as I write you! They are filled with the little life that passes within the women's courtyard. It is all the life I know. My world is bounded by these walls, and I ask no more.

I am your loving wife.

My Dear One,

All your womenfolk have been shopping! A most unheard-of event for us. We have Li-ti to thank for this great pleasure, because, but for her, the merchants would have brought their goods to the courtyard for us to make our choice. Li-ti would not hear of that; she wanted to see the city, and she wanted to finger the pretty goods within the shops. She knew exactly what she wished, and life was made uncomfortable for us all until your Mother ordered the chairs and we went into the city. We were a long procession. First,

the August One with her four-bearer chair; then your most humble wife, who has only two bearers—as yet; then Li-ti; and after her Mah-li, followed by the chairs of the servants who came to carry back our purchases.

It was most exciting for all of us, as we go rarely within the city gate. It was market day, and the streets were made more narrow by the baskets of fish and vegetables that lined the way. The flat stones of the pavements were slippery and it seemed our bearers could not find a way amongst the crowd of riders on horses and small donkeys, the coolies with their buckets of hot water swinging from their shoulders, the sweetmeat sellers, the men with bundles, and the women with small baskets. They all stepped to one side at the sound of the *Ah-yo* of our leader, except a band of coolies carrying the monstrous trunk of a pine tree, chanting as they swung the mast between them, and keeping step with the chant. It seemed a solemn dirge, as if some great giant were being carried to the resting place of the dead.

But sadness could not come to us when shopping, and our eager eyes looked long at the signs above the open shopways. There were long black signs of lacquer with letters of raised gold, or red ones with the characters carved and gilded. Above a shoe shop was a boot made for the King of the Mountains, and in front of a pipe shop was a water pipe fit for his mate. From the fan shop hung delicate, gilded fans; and framing the silk shop windows gaily colored silk was draped in rich festoons that nearly swept the pathway.

We bought silks and satins and gay brocades, we chatted and we bargained and we shopped. We handled jade and pearls and ornaments of twisted gold, and we priced amulets and incense pots and gods. We filled our eyes with luxury and our *amahs'* [maids'] chairs with packages, and returned home three happy, tired, hungry

women, thinking with longing of the hissing tea urn upon the charcoal brazier.

That crowded, bustling, threatening city seems another world
from this, our quiet, walled-in dwelling. I feel that here we are protected, cared for, guarded, and life's hurry and distress will only
pass us by, not touch us. Yet—we like to see it all, and know that
we are a part of that great wonder-thing, the world.

I am your happy, tired
Wife

My Dear One,

I am carrying a burden for another that is causing me much sorrow. Do you remember Chen-peh, who is from my province and
who married Ling Peh-yu about two moons after I came to your
household? She came to me yesterday in dire distress. She is being
returned to her home by her husband's people, and, as you know, if
a woman is divorced shame covers her until her latest hour. I am
inexpressibly saddened, as I do not know what can be done. The

trouble is with his mother and, I fear, her own pride of family. She cannot forget that she comes from a great house, and she is filled with pride at the recollection of her home. I have told her that the father and mother of one's husband should be honored beyond her own. I can see that she has failed in respect; and thus she merits condemnation. We have all learned as babes that "respect" is the first word in the book of wisdom. I know it is hard at times to still the tongue, but all paths that lead to peace are hard.

She will remain with me two nights. Last night she lay wide-eyed, staring into the darkness, with I know not what within her soul. I begged her to think wisely, to talk frankly with her husband and his mother, to whom she owes obedience. There should be not pride where love is. She must think upon the winter of her days, when she will be alone, without husband and without children, eating bitter rice of charity, though 'tis given by her people. I put her in remembrance of that saying of the poetry:

> Rudely torn may be a cotton mantle,
>   yet a skillful hand may join it;
> Snapped may be the string where pearls are threaded,
>   yet the thread all swiftly knotted;
> But a husband and his wife, once parted,
>   never more may meet.

I must not bring you the sorrows of another. Oh, dear one, there will never come between you and me the least small river of distrust. I will bear to you no double heart, and you will cherish me and love me always.

Your Wife

9

My Dear One,

I cannot wait until the seventh day to write to you again, as my letter to you yestereve was full of sadness and longing. Now I have slept, and troubles from a distance do not seem so grave.

Your Honorable Mother has chided me gravely, but to my mind unjustly, and, as you know, I could not answer her words, though they pierced me "like arrows of white winged bows." Poor Li-ti is in trouble again, and this time she has brought it upon herself, yet she cannot be blamed. I, as a head of the household, as your Honorable Mother has told me, should have protected her. I told you that she brought servants from her old home, and amongst them her childhood's nurse, who, I am sure, loves Li-ti dearly; but, as many women who have little to occupy their hands, she loves to sit in the women's courtyard and gossip. If it had stopped within the servants' courtyard all would have been well; but at the time of Li-ti's dressing all the small goods she had gathered during the day were emptied into the lap of Li-ti, who is too young to know that "as poison that reaches the blood spreads through the body, so does the love of gossip spread through the soul of woman." I do not know how it came about, but comparisons were made between the households, that of her home and that of her husband, and news was carried back to the servants' quarters until at last our household was in a state of unrest that stopped all work and made living quite impossible.

It seems small, but it is the retelling of little calumnies that dis-

G
o
l
∂
e
n

L
i
l
i
e
∂

turbs the harmony of kinsmen and ruins the peace of families. Finally I found it necessary to talk to Li-ti's nurse, and I told her many things it was good for her to know. I warned her that if she did not wish to revisit her home province she must still her tongue. Things were better for a time, but they all commenced again, and I called her to my courtyard and said to her, "The sheaves of rice have been beaten across the wood for the last time. You must go." Li-ti was inconsolable, but I was firm. Such quarrels are not becoming when we are so many beneath one rooftree.

The servant went away, but she claimed her servant's right of reviling us within our gate. She lay beneath our outer archway for three long hours and called down curses upon the Liu family. One could not get away from the sound of the enumeration of the faults and vices of your illustrious ancestors even behind closed doors. I did not know, my husband, that history claimed so many men of action by the name of Liu. It pleased me to think you may claim so long a lineage, as she went back to the dynasty of Ming and brought forth from his grave each poor man and woman and told us of—not his virtues. I should have been more indignant, perhaps, if I had not heard overmuch of the wonders of your family tree. I was impressed by the amount of knowledge acquired by the family of Li-ti. They must have searched the chronicles, which evidently recorded only the unworthy acts of your menfolk in the past. I hope that I will forget what I have heard, as sometime when I am trying to escape from your ancestors the tongue might become unruly.

At the end of three hours the woman was faint and very ill. I had one of the servants take her down to the boat, and sent a man home with her, bearing a letter saying she was sickening for home faces. She is old, and I did not want her to end her days in disgrace and shame.

27

But your Honorable Mother! Your Honorable Mother! Are you not glad that you are in a far-off country? She went from courtyard to courtyard, and for a time I fully expected she would send to the *Yamen* [official residence] for the soldiers; then she realized the woman was within her right, and so restrained herself. It nearly caused her death, as you know your Honorable Mother has not long practiced the virtue of restraint, especially of the tongue. She was finally overcome and taken to her chamber, and we brought her tea and heated wine, and tried in all our ways to make her forget the great humiliation. As she became no better, we sent for the man of medicine from the Eastern Gate, and he wished to burn her shoulders with a heated *can* [cup] to remove the heat within her. To this she objected so strongly that he hastily gathered his utensils and departed, looking fearfully over his shoulder from time to time as he passed quickly down the hillside.

Then I thought of her favorite priest from the monastery down below, and sent for him. He came with candle and incense and, I think, some rose wine for which the monastery is justly famous; and he chanted prayers, striking from time to time a little gong, until peace was restored and sleep came to her eyelids.

In the morning she wished to talk to Li-ti; but I feared for her, and I said, "You cannot speak of the ocean to a well frog, nor sing of ice to a summer insect. She will not understand." She said Li-ti was without brains, a senseless thing of paint and powder. I said, "We will form her, we will make of her a wise woman in good time." She replied with bitterness, "Rotten wood cannot be carved nor walls of dirt be plastered." I could not answer, but I sent Li-ti to pass the day with Chih-peh at the Goldfish Temple, and when she returned the time was not so stormy.

All this made me unhappy, and the cares of this great household pressed heavily upon my shoulders. Please do not think the cares too heavy, nor that I do not crave the work. I know all labor is done for the sake of happiness, and whether the happiness comes or not, I find less time to dream and mourn and long for you, my husband.

Your Wife

My Dear One,

We have been to a great festival at the Temple of the Goddess of a Thousand Hands. Your Honorable Mother decided that we should go by boat part of the way, so the chairs were told to meet us at the Western Village Rest House.

We hired from the city one of those great pleasure boats, but it was not too great for us all. There was the August One, and four of her friends, then Li-ti, Mah-li, and myself. We took the cook, the steward, and three *amahs*, and it was indeed a time of feasting. It was the first time I had been upon the canal, and it was different from seeing it from the terrace. As we passed slowly along we could watch the life of the water people. On the banks were the great waterwheels turned by the village buffalo. In the deserted districts women were gathering reeds to make the sleeping mats and boat

covers. The villages with their blue-gray houses and thatched roofs nestling among the groves of bamboo looked like chicklets sheltering under the outstretched wings of the mother hen.

We pushed our way through the crowded waterways of the cities, where we could catch glimpses of the guests in the teahouses or the keepers of the shops, or could watch the children leaning over the balconies. On the steps between the houses that led to the waterside women were washing clothes or the dyers were cleansing the extra dye from the blue cotton that clothes all China's poor. We caught small bits of gossip and heard the laughter of all these people, who seemed happy at their work.

When we could again pass to the open canal we would watch the boats. I did not know there were so many boats in all the world. They floated slowly past us—big boats, little boats, those that went by sail, and those that went by oar. There were the boats of mandarins and merchants, those for passengers, and great unwieldy boats for rice. We saw the fishing boats with their hungry, fierce-eyed cormorants sitting quietly in their places, waiting for the master to send them diving into the water for the fish they may not eat.

The canal was a great broad highway. Even the towpaths had their patrons. Travelers on wheelbarrows, rich men in sedan chairs, soldiers, coolies, chanting as they tramped along with their burdens swinging from the bamboo on their shoulders, all going to or coming from the great city to which we drew nearer with each stroke.

At the rest house the bearers were awaiting us, and we were carried up the long paved roadway to the temple. It seemed as if all the world had turned to praying—all the world of women, that is. They were here, rich and poor, peasant and official's wife, but in the temple all of a sisterhood. We descended from our chairs in the courtyard and put our spirit money in the great burner, where it ascended in tiny flames side by side with that of the beggar women, to the great God in the Heavens. We entered the temple, placed our candles, and lighted our incense. We made our obeisance to the Many-Handed Goddess and asked her blessing on our household for the year to come. Then I went to the Mother of Mercies, Kwan-yin, and made my deepest reverence, because for her my heart is full of love and gratitude. The other gods I respect and make them all due worship, but I feel they are far away from me. Kwan-yin is the woman's God, and I feel her love for me. She shapes my way, and I know it is to her I owe it that my life flows on as a gentle stream, and I know that she cares for me and guards me now that you are away and I have no one on whom to lean. She is my Kwan-yin, my Mother of Mercy, and each day I do some little deed for her, some little thing to show remembrance, so she will know the hours are not too full or the days too short for me to place my offering on an altar built of love.

As we turned to leave the temple I glanced back at the great dark chamber and I saw the God of Light, the Buddha, sitting there so calm upon his throne, with the light of many candles before him and clouds of incense that floated to the roof. I thought, "He is all powerful. I only prayed to him out of my lips, not with my heart. Perhaps—" So I returned. I prayed the mighty God with humble prayer to bring my loved one swiftly home to me; and then we left the temple. We walked slowly through the courtyards, looking at the great trees that stood like tall, grim sentinels guarding the place of prayer. Then we were taken by our bearers to the Goldfish Monastery in the hills. Do you remember it? You and I were there once in the springtime.

We bought the small round cakes from the priests and fed the greedy fish. They swarmed over the pool, pushing, nudging, fighting one another to get the morsels we threw them. Tiring of that, we had tea and sweetmeats served upon the terrace; then, after chatting for a time, we left for the boat. We drifted slowly homeward. Your Mother and her friends discussed the earth, the moon, the sun and stars, as well as smaller matters, such as children, husbands, servants, schools—and as you know, it is a sore subject with her, this matter of the new education. I heard her say: "All my sons have book knowledge. Of what use is it in the end? The cock crows and the dog barks. We know that, but the wisest of my sons cannot say why one crows and the other barks, nor why they crow or bark at all." Can you hear her, and see her shake her head dolefully over the dismal fact that you have left the narrow way of Confucius and the classics?

We came to the pathway just at sunset, and as I looked up at the old palace a little hurt came to my heart that you were not close by my side. It lay so peaceful there and quiet, the curving roofs like flights of doves who had settled down with their wings not yet quite folded. It brought remembrance that for me it was an empty palace. I will see no one—as Li-ti will—within the archway.

Your Wife Who Loves You

My Dear One,

Your letter and the photographs received. You say it is a "flash-light" of a reception to your master, the prince. I do not know exactly what that means, but there seem to be many people and—ladies. I have not shown your Honorable Mother the picture, as she might ask you to return at once. I do not criticize your friends, nor could our prince go to a place not fitting to his dignity, but—the ladies seem in my poor judgment most lightly clad.

The papers here are full of your reception in that foreign land and of the honor that is paid the embassy. Your brother read to all within the courtyard of the feasts that are given in honor of His Highness, and we were full proud, knowing well you stood close by him at the time. Your letters are a joy to me. We read them many times, and then I read those you sent to Chih-peh, which talk of things I do not understand. You must not give the boy foolish ideas, as he prates the most glibly of "republics" and "government of the people by the people," after he has received your letters. That is for men of wisdom like you, but not for foolish boys to carry with them to the teahouse.

Kwei-li

12

My Dear One,

You asked me if I still care for you, if the remembrance of your face has grown less dear with the passing of days. Dear one, you know we Chinese women are not supposed to know of love, much less to speak of it. We read of it, we know it is the song of all the world, but it comes not to us unless by chance. We go to you as strangers, we have no choice, and if the gods withhold their greatest gift, the gift of love, then life is gray and wan as the twilight of a hopeless day. Few women have the joy I feel when I look into my loved one's face and know that I am his and he is mine, and that our lives are twined together for all the days to come.

Do I love you? I cannot tell. I think of you by day and I dream of you by night. I never want to hurt you or cause you a moment's sorrow. I would fill my hands with happiness to lay down at your feet. You are my life, my love, my all, and I am yours to hold through all the years.

My Dear One,

It is the time of school, and now all the day from the servants' courtyard I hear their droning voices chanting the sayings of Confucius. I did not know we had so many young lives within our compound until I saw them all seated at their tables. I go at times and tell them tales—which they much prefer to lessons—but of which your Honorable Mother does not approve. I told them the other day of Pan-gu. Do you remember him? How at the beginning of Time the great god Pan-gu with hammer and chisel formed the earth? He toiled and he worked for eighteen thousand years, and each day increased in stature six feet, and, to give him room, the Heavens rose and the earth became larger and larger. When the Heavens were round and the earth all smooth, he died. His head became mountains, his breath the wind and the clouds, his voice the thunder. His arms and legs were the four poles, his veins the rivers, his muscles the hills and his flesh the fields. His eyes became the stars, his skin and hair the herbs and the trees, and the insects that touched him became people. Does not that make you think of childhood's days?

They crowd around me and say, "Tell us more," just as I did with my old *amah* when she quieted me with the tales of the gods. Yesterday, one small boy, the son of the chief steward, begged for a story of the sun. I had to tell him that my wisdom did not touch the sun, although I, in my foolish heart, think it a great god because it gives us warmth and we can feel its kindly rays. I said, "You have seen the coolies tracking on the towpath with their heavy, wadded clothing wet with rain. If it were not for the kindly sun that dries them, how could they toil and work and drag the great rice boats up to the watergate? Is he not a god to them?"

I told them also of Chang-ngo, the great, great beauty who drank the cup of life eternal. She went to the moon, where the jealous gods turned her into a great black toad. She is there, forever thinking, mourning over her lost beauty, and when we see the soft haze come over the face of the moon, we know that she is weeping and filling the space with her tears.

I perhaps am wrong to tell the foolish tales to the children, but they grow so tired of the hard benches and Chang-tai, the teacher, who glares at them so fiercely when they don't speak quickly enough to please him.

There has been much gossip from the valley over the mountainside. It seems an iron bridge is being put across the river, and strange men come and peer at the countryside through witch glasses. It has made the good spirits of the air draw apart from the valley, and the cattle have died and the rice not ripened, and much sorrow has been broadcast. The river overflowed, because they desecrated the dragon's back by digging down into the sacred earth. I know nothing except what is brought from the marketplace, and, as it does not concern us here on the mountainside, I listen only with my ears, not with my mind.

The nights are long and cold. The moon casts silver shimmering lights over the valley below. We cannot stand long on the terrace but must stay close within our rooms near to the charcoal braziers. The wind sweeps over the rooftree with the wailing voice of a woman.

Oh, Soul of Mine, with weary heart the creeping days I'm counting.

Your Wife

My Dear One,

We have had a serious sickness come to all the countryside; rich and poor, peasant and merchant have suffered from a fever that will not abate. It raged for more than a moon before its cause was known. Do you remember Kwan-lin Pagoda? Its ruin has long been a standing shame to the people of the province, and finally the gods have resented their neglect and sent them this great illness. Over all the city the yellow edicts of the priests have been places so as to meet the eye of all who travel. They are in the marketplaces, at the entrance of the teahouses, standing on great boards at the doorways of the temples, in front of the watergates, and at each city postern.

They state that the gods are angry and send to each manor household that will not give three days' work to the pagoda the fever that leaves one weak and ailing. They demand the labor of the city; and if it is not given freely, toil is sent the people in their sleep and they waken weary, and must so remain until the work is finished.

We did not hearken to the summons until Chih-peh, your brother, fell ill with the sickness. He grew worse each day, until Li-ti and your Honorable Mother were panic-stricken. At last the chairs were ordered, and your Mother and I went to the monastery on the hillside to consult with the old abbot, who is most full of wisdom. Your Honorable Mother told him of the illness that had assailed her son, and begged him to tell her if it were the illness of the pagoda. He meditated long and seriously, then he said, "My daughter, the gods are no respecter of persons; they wish service from your son." "But," your Honorable Mother objected, "he is no workman. He cannot labor upon the pagoda." The abbot said, "There are more ways of giving service than the labor of the hands. The gods will allow him to contribute his wealth and buy the toil of other men, and thus he may cancel his obligation." The August One satisfied the greedy heart of the priest, and then he told her to go and make her obeisance to the God of Light, the great Buddha, and see what message he had for her.

She took the hollow bamboo filled with the numbered slices of wood and, prostrating herself three times before the Great One, shook it slowly until one detached itself from its brothers and fell to the floor. The abbot then handed her a slip of paper that read:

> Wisdom sits by the Western Gate
> And gives health and happiness to those
>   who wait.

These words meant nothing to your Honorable Mother; and after giving the abbot more silver, he said, "Beside the Western Gate sits the owl of wisdom, the great doctor Chow-fong. His father and his father's father were wise; their study was mankind, and to him has come all their stores of knowledge. He has books of wonderful age, which tell him the secret of the world. Go to him; he will give you the plan of healing."

We started for the Western Gate, and I, in my wicked heart, spoke thoughts that should have been closely locked within my breast. I said, "Perhaps the doctor and the priest have formed a combination most profitable to the two. If we had gone to the doctor first, we might have been sent to the abbot." It was a great mistake to mention such a dreadful thing, and I realized it instantly; as you know, the Elder One, your mother, has a tongue of eloquence, and I was indeed glad that her bearers carried her at least ten paces from my bearers—and the way was long.

Even your Honorable Mother was awed at the solemn looks of this great man of medicine who, in his dim room with dried bats hanging from the ceiling beams and a dragon's egg close by his hand, glared at her through his great goggles like a wise old owl. She apologized for disturbing so great a man at his studies, but she was the bearer of a message from the abbot. He read it carefully, then took down a monstrous book entitled *The Golden Mirror of Medical Practice*, and solemnly pored over its pages. At last he wrote upon a paper, then chanted:

> In a building tall, by the city wall,
> In the street of the Tower of Gold,
> Is the plant of health, long life and wealth,
> In the claws of the Dragon bold.

The August One took the paper, laid some silver upon the table, and we hurried from his doorway, glad to be free from his fearful presence. When we entered the chairs and looked to the paper for directions to give the bearers, the characters were meaningless to us. I repeated his chant, and the head bearer said, "There is a shop of drugs in the street of the Tower of Gold, and the sign of the place is a Golden Dragon's Claw."

We soon were there, and waited in our chairs while the bearer took the paper into the maker of medicines. We waited long, and your Honorable Mother would have been impatient if sleep had not kindly made her forget the waiting hours. I, sitting in my chair, could look through the archways into the big covered courtyards where blind men were grinding herbs. They were harnessed to great stones, and went round and round all day, like buffalo at the water-wheel. I wondered why the gods had put them at this service. What sins had they committed in their other life, to be compelled to work like beasts, grinding the herbs that would bring health and life to others, while they lived on in darkness? Often I would hear the soft call of the deer as they moved restlessly in their tiny cells. I know their horns, when powdered fine with beetles' wings, are the cure for fevers and all ailments of the blood, but why could not the wise ones of the earth have found some herb or weed to take their place and give these wild ones of the woods their freedom? Finally, the bearer came with a tiny jar, too small, it seemed, to take such time in mixing, and we returned to the waiting Li-ti.

The medicine was black and nasty and smelled not sweetly, which proved its strength. Chih-peh slowly got better, and the world again looked fair to Li-ti, and the song came to her lips. The flowers were put in her hair, the gay dresses were brought out of their boxes, and she was, as of old, our butterfly.

K
w
e
i
.

l
i

We laughed at her for her fright, but I thought, if it had been you who was ill, and I did not know the cure! Oh, dear one, do you understand that, to a woman who loves, her husband is more than Heaven, more than herself? All that she is not, all that she lacks, all that she desires to be, is her beloved. His breath alone can bring peace to her heart. And it is he alone who teaches her the depth of passionate joy there is in love and life and all things beautiful.

I am your wife

15

My Dear One,

Your Honorable Mother is beset by the desire of marrying. No, do not start; it is not of herself she is thinking. She will go to the River of Souls mourning your Honorable Father, and a *pailo* [decorative archway] will be erected in her honor. It is of her household she is thinking. She says our rooftree is too small to shelter four women, three of whom have little brains—and that includes your humble, loving wife—but why she should wish to exchange Mah-li, whom she knows, for a strange woman she does not know, passes my understanding. She seems not overfond of daughters-in-law, if one can judge from chance remarks.

First, before I speak of Mah-li, I must tell you of your brother. Your Honorable Mother is right—it were better that he marry and have a heel rope that leads him homeward. He is unruly and passes overmuch time at the Golden Lotus Teahouse. He is not bad or wicked. He lives but for the moment, and the moment is often wine flushed. He will not work or study, and many times at night I send away the gatekeeper and leave my *amah* at the outer archway, so your Mother will not know the hour he enters. He is young, and has chosen friends not equal to himself, and they have set his feet in the pathway that slopes downward.

He does not wish to marry. We have told him that marriage is a will of the gods and must be obeyed. "Man does not attain the one-winged birds of our childhood's tale, they must rise together." It is useless to talk to him. A spark of fire will not kindle wood that is still too green, and I fear he is in love with life, and youth, and freedom.

I do not wish to doubt the wisdom of the August One, but I think she made a mistake in her choice of a bride for your brother, Chih-mo. She chose Tai-lo, the daughter of the Prefect of Chih-li. The arrangements were nearly made, the dowry had even been discussed, but when the astrologer cast their horoscopes to see if they could pass their life in peace together, it was found that the ruler of Chih-mo's life was a lion, and that of the bride's, a swallow—so it was clearly seen they could not share one rooftree. I fear (I would not have this come to the ears of your Honorable Mother) that some silver was left upon the doorstep of the astrologer. Chih-mo asked of me the loan of a hundred *taels*, and I saw the wife of the reader of the stars pass by with a new gown of red-and-gold brocade.

I think Chih-mo had seen Tai-lo. Report gives her small beauty. Yet, as the Elder One says, "Musk is known by its perfume, and not by the druggist's label." Quite likely she would have made a good wife; and—we have one beauty in the household—it is enough.

K
w
e
i
.
l
i

There is much wailing in the courtyards. The gardener and the bearer and the watchman are having the feet of their small daughters bound. The saying "For every pair of golden lilies there is a *kang* [barrel] of tears" is true. I am sorry for them. Just when they want to run and play, they must sit all day with aching feet. My *amah* wished to put on the heavy bindings, but I would not permit it. I said, "Do you want little eyes to fill with tears each time they see you coming across the courtyard? If their grandmothers do not come, let some old women from the village do the cruel thing."

The happy rains of the spring are here. It is not the cold, dreary rain of autumn, but dancing, laughing rain that comes sweeping across the valley, touching the rice fields lovingly, and bringing forth the young green leaves of the mulberry. I hear it patter upon the roof at nighttime, and in the morning all the earth seems cleansed and new; fresh colors greet my eyes when I throw back my casement.

When will you come to me, keeper of my heart?

Your Wife

Dear One,

1 6

He whose faults are never told him
Doubtless deems the angels mold him.

That cannot be said of three women of your household.

It is Mah-li this time on whom the wrath descends. She and Li-ti were embroidering in the western room where they could get the last rays of the sun. Perhaps they were speaking on forbidden subjects—I do not know; but your Honorable Mother entered quietly and reproved them, and (even when I write it I blush for her) Mah-li said to her Honorable Mother, "Only cats and cranes and thieves walk silently." Your Mother was speechless with anger, and justly so, and now it is decided that Mah-li must be married. She needs a stronger hand than a woman's. Is it not ridiculous, little Mah-li needing a strong hand?

At first the August One considered Meng-wheh, the prefect at Sung-dong. He is old and cross, but when I remonstrated, I was told that he was rich. His many tens of thousands of *cycee* are supposed to weigh more than youth and love. I said, "Though he bar with gold his silver door," a man cannot keep the wife who loves him not. Your Honorable Mother thought more wisely, and after many days of consideration entered into consultation with the family of Sheng Ta-jen in regard to his son. It seems Mah-li is doomed to marriage soon, and she does not know whether she is happy or sor-

G
o
l
∂
e
n

L
i
l
i
e
∂

rowful. She is turned this way and that, as the seed of the cotton tree is swayed by the coming and going of the wind. Today she laughs, tomorrow she weeps. Your Mother has lost all patience with her, and, as she always does when her own words fail her, I heard her quoting the Sage: "Just as ducks' legs though short cannot be lengthened without pain, nor cranes' legs though long be shortened without misery to the crane, neither can sense be added to a silly woman's head."

I feel that your Honorable Mother is unkind to Mah-li. She is a flower, a flower that has her place in life the same as the morning glory, which is loved just as fondly by the gods as the pine tree that stands so stately upon the hillside. She is light and pure and dainty as the fragrance of perfumed air, and I do not want to see her go to a family who will not understand her youth and love of play.

Mah-li has asked me of money, and with it bought a great candle for each day, which she sends down the mountainside to be placed before Kwan-yin. I asked her to tell me her prayer, which needed so large an offering. The unfilial girl said she prayed, "Kwan-yin, send me a husband with *no* family."

Such a lot of petty gossip I pour into your ears, yet you would know the happenings of your household. Of the world outside, your brother writes you. My world is here within these walls.

Your Wife

.

.

.

.

17

My Dear One,

Your house is a house of intrigue. Deep, dark intrigue and plotting. Your wife has lent herself to a most unwomanly thing, and doubtless you will tell her so, but Mah-li begged so prettily, I could refuse her nothing. I told you in my last letter that your Honorable Mother had been regarding the family of Sheng Ta-jen with a view to his son as husband of Mah-li. It is settled, and Mah-li leaves us in the autumn. None of us except Chih-peh has seen the young man, and Mah-li did a most immodest thing the other day. She came to me and asked me to find out from Chih-peh if he were handsome, if he were young—all the questions that burn the tongue of a young girl, but that she must keep within tightly closed lips if she would not be thought unmaidenly. I asked your brother; but his reply did not answer the questions Mah-li wished to know. So we arranged a plan that caused me many nights of sleeplessness. It was carried out and—still the sky is blue, the stars are bright at night, and the moon shines just as softly on the valley.

The first part of the plan was for Li-ti. She tried to persuade Chih-peh to ask Shen-go to spend the day with him at the Fir Tree Monastery. When he knew the meaning of the invitation, he refused. He was shocked, and properly; as it was a thing unheard of. He could not understand why Mah-li would not be content with her mother's choice. Li-ti brought all her little ways to bear—and Chih-peh can refuse her nothing. At the Feast of the Moon your brother asked three friends to join him at the monastery and stroll amongst the groves.

The rest of the plan was for me to carry out; and I, your wife, displayed a talent for diplomacy. I noticed that the cheeks of our Honorable Mother were pale, that she seemed listless, that her step was wearied. I said doubtless she was tired of being shut within the compound walls with three aimless, foolish women, and proposed a feast or pilgrimage. I mentioned the Goldfish Pond, knowing she was tired of it; spoke of the Pagoda on the Hills, knowing full well that she did not like the priests therein; then, by chance, read from a book the story of the two kings. It is the tale of the King of Hangchow and the King of Soochow who, in the olden time, divided our great valley between them. The King of Hangchow was an old man, and the cares of state fell heavily upon his shoulders. The King of Soochow was a young man, eaten up with mad ambitions. He began to tread upon the lands of the old king, taking now a farmhouse, now a village, and at last a city, until the poor old king was threatened at his very gateway by the army of the young man. The young king had strength, but the old king had guile, so he made a peace with his enemy for one year. He sent him presents, costly silks and teas, and pearls and jade and ginseng, and, last and best, a beautiful slave girl, the most beautiful in the province. The young king was delighted, and forgot his warring, passing all his days within the women's quarters.

As the winter waned and the spring came, the slave girl sickened, said she panted for the hillsides, and she pointed to the mountain outside the city walls. He was a foolish king, and he built a palace for her, and she moved there with her women. The king was lonely in the city, and he passed his days with the women in the

palace on the mountain. While living there in pleasure, and his army in the city, the old King of Hangchow sent his soldiers; and soon there was no King of Soochow, only a slave girl decked with many jewels, who was taken back with honor to the old king's city.

I read all this to your Honorable Mother, and told her we could see the ruins of the fish pond, of the palace, see the fallen marbles from the teahouse, and—the chairs were ordered, and we went. We wandered over deserted pathways, saw the lotus pools once filled with goldfish, picked our way through lonely courtyards, climbed the sunken steps of terraces that had once been gay with flowers. It all was melancholy, this place built for pleasure, now a mass of crumbling ruins, and it saddened us. We sat upon the king's bench that overlooked the plain, and from it I pointed out the Fir Tree Monastery in the distance. I spoke of their famous tea, sun dried with the flowers of jessamine, and said it might bring cheer and take away the gloom caused by the sight of death and vanished grandeur now around us.

We were carried swiftly along the pathways that wound in and out past farm villages and rest houses until we came to the monastery, which is like a yellow jewel in its setting of green fir trees. The priests made us most welcome, and we drank of their tea, which has not been overpraised, sitting at a great open window looking down upon the valley. Strolling in the courtyard was Chih-peh with his friends. Mah-li never raised her eyes; she sat as maidens sit in public, but—she saw.

We came home by another pathway, to pass the resting place of Sheng-dong, the man who at the time of famine fed the poor and gave his help to all the needy. The gods so loved him that when his body was carried along the roadway to the resting place of his Ancestors, all the stones stood up to pay him reverence. One can see them now, standing straight and stiff, as if waiting for his command to lie down again.

Are you dissatisfied with me? Have I done wrong? Dear One, it means so much to Mah-li. Let her dream these months of waiting. It is hard to keep wondering, doubting, fearing one knows not what, hoping as young girls hope. But now she has seen him. To me he was just a straight-limbed, bright-faced boy; to her he is a god. There are no teeth so white, no hair so black, and a man were not born who walked with such a noble stride. It will make the summer pass more quickly, and the thought of the marriage chair will not be to her the gateway of a prison.

Are you not tired of that far-off country? Each time I break the seal of your dear letter I say, "Perhaps this time—it holds for me my happiness. It will say, 'I am coming home to you.'" I am longing for that message.

Your Wife

My Dear One,

It will soon be the Feast of the Springtime. Even now the roads are covered with the women coming to the temple carrying their baskets of spirit money and candles to lay before the Buddha.

Spring will soon be truly here; the buds are everywhere. Everything laughs from the sheer joy of laughter. The sun looks down upon the water on the canal and it breaks into a thousand little ripples from pure gladness. I too am happy, and I want to give of my happiness. I have put a great *kang* of tea down by the rest house on the towpath, so that they who thirst may drink. Each morning I send Chang-tai, the gatekeeper, down to the man who lives in the little reed hut he has built by the grave of his father. For three years he will live there, to show the world his sorrow. I think it very worthy and filial of him, so I send him rice each morning. I have also done another thing to express the joy that is deep within my heart. The old abbot, out of thankfulness that the tall poles were not erected before the monastery gateway, has turned the fields back of the temple into a freeing place for animals. There one may acquire merit by buying a sheep, a horse, a dog, a bird, or a snake that is to be killed, and turning it loose where it may live and die a natural death, as the gods intended from the beginning. I have given him a sum of money, large in his eyes but small when compared to my happiness, to aid him in this worthy work. I go over in the morning and look at the poor horses and dogs, and wonder whose soul is regarding me from out of their tired eyes.

Let me hear that you are coming, man of mine, and I will gather dewdrops from the cherry trees and bathe me in their perfume to give me beauty that will hold you close to me.

I am,
Your Wife

19

My Dear One,

I have received your letter telling me you will not be here until the summer comes. Then, I must tell you my news, as the spring-time is here, the flowers are budding, the grass is green, soon the plum tree in the courtyard will be white. I am jealous of this paper that will see the delight and joy in your eyes. In the evening I watch the rice boats pass along the canal, where the water is green and silvery like the new leaves of the willow, and I say, "Perhaps when you return, I shall be the mother of a child." Ah!—I have told you. Does it bring you happiness, my lord? Does it make a quick little catch in your breath? Does your pulse quicken at the thought that soon you will be a father?

You will never know what it has meant to me. It has made the creature live that was within my soul, and my whole being is bathed with its glory. You will never know how many times I have gone down the pathway to the temple and asked this great boon of our Lady of Mercy. She granted it, and my life is made perfect. I am indeed a woman, fulfilling a woman's destiny. If a woman bear not sons for her lord, what is her life worth? Do we not know that the first of the seven causes for putting away a wife is that she brings no sons into the world to worship at the graves of her husband's ancestors? But I, Kwei-li—that will not be said of me.

Sometimes I think, "If something should happen; if the gods should be jealous of my happiness and I should not see you again?" Then the heart of the woman throbs with fear, and I throw myself

at the feet of Kwan-yin and beg for strength. She gives me peace
and brings to my remembrance that the bond of fate is sealed within
the moon. There is no place for fear, for anything but love; my
heart is so filled with its happiness.

Your Wife

My Dear One,

The spring has come, and with it some new pulse of life beats
through my quiet veins. I spend long hours upon the terrace,
breathing in the perfume of the many flowers. The cherry blossoms
are a glory. The whole steep hillside is covered with a fairy lace, as
if some god knew how we hungered after the beauty and gave us
these pink blossoms to help us to forget the bare cold earth of
winter.

It is the time of praying, and all the women with their candles
and their incense are bending knees and chanting prayers to
Kwan-yin for the blessing of a son. There is a pilgrimage to the
Kwem-li Pagoda. I can see it in the distance, with its lotus bells that
sway and ring with each light breath of wind. One does not think of
it as a thing of brick and mortar, or as a many-storied temple, but
as a casket whose jewels are the prayers of waiting, hoping women.

You ask me how I pass my days? I cannot tell. At dawn, I wake
with hope and listen to the song of the meadowlark. At noon, I

20

dream of my great happiness to come. At sunset, I am swept away into the land of my golden dreams, into the heart of my golden world that is peopled with but three—You, Him, and Me. I am drifting happily, sleepily, forgetting care, waiting for the gods to bring me joy.

Your Wife

21

My Dear One,

My courtyard is filled with the sounds of chatting women. I have sent for the sewing women and those who do embroidery, and the days are passed in making little garments. We are all so busy; Li-ti, Mah-li, even your Honorable Mother takes again the needle and shows us how she embroidered jackets for you when you were young. The piles of clothing grow each day, and I touch them and caress them and imagine I can see them folding close a tiny form. There are jackets, trousers, shoes, tiny caps, and thick warm blankets.

I send for Blind Chun, the storyteller, and he makes the hours pass quickly with his tales of bygone days. The singers and the fortune-tellers all have found the path that leads up to our gateway, knowing they will find a welcome.

I am,
Your Happy Wife

I send you cherry blossoms. They grew within your courtyard, and each tiny petal will bring to you remembrance of your wife who loves you well.

If you could see my courtyard! It seems carpeted with snow, so many are the cherry blossoms on its pavement. They say I am untidy that I permit it to be untouched by broom or brush. It is clean and spotless all the year, save at this the time of cherry blossoms, when it is untrodden and unswept.

I cannot write you merely household cares and gossip. I am so filled with happiness, I can only dream and wonder. Joy is beating with his wings just outside my open window, and soon all the gates of Heaven will be opened wide to me.

Your Wife

<table>
<tr><td>2 4</td><td>He is here, beloved, your son! I put out my hand and touch him, and the breath of the wind through the pine trees brings the music of the gods to me. He is big and strong and beautiful. I see in his eyes as in a mirror the reflection of your dear face, and I know he is yours and mine, and we three are one. He is my joy, my son, my firstborn. I am tired, my lord, the brush is heavy, but it is such a happy, happy tired.</td></tr>
</table>

Your Wife

<table>
<tr><td>2 5</td><td>Is there anything so wonderful as being the mother of a son? I simply sing, and laugh, and live — oh, how I *live* the long days through. I have happiness enough for all the world, and I want to give and give and give. Your mother says that all the beggars within the province know there is rice outside our gateway; but when I look into my son's eyes, and feel his tiny fingers groping at my neck, I feel I must give of my plenty to those who have no joy.</td></tr>
</table>

Oh, husband of mine, come back and see your son!

Do you know what love is? You cannot till you hold Love itself within your very arms. I thought I loved you. I smile now at the remembrance of that feeble flickering flame that was as like unto real love as the faint, cold beam of the candle is to the rays of the glorious sun. Now—now—you are the father of my son. You have a new place in my heart. The tie that binds our hearts together is stronger than a rope of twisted bamboo, it is a bond, a love bond, which never can be severed. I am the mother of your firstborn—you have given me my man-child. Love you—love you!—now I *know*!

I am Your Own

I am angry with your brother Chih-peh. He is a man of very small discernment. He does not see the wonders of your son. He says he cannot see that he is a child of more than mortal beauty. I am sorry for him. The gods have surely drawn a film before his eyes.

But I cannot bear resentment, there is no room in me for anything but love and the days are far too short to hold my happiness.

I pass them near my baby. I croon to him sweet lullabies at which
the others laugh. I say, "You do not understand? Of course not, it
is the language of the gods," and as he sleeps I watch his small face
grow each day more like to yours. I spend long hours thinking of
his future. He must be a man like you, strong, noble, kindly, bearing your great name with honor, so that in years to come it will be
said, "The firstborn son of Kwei-li was a great and worthy man."

At night I lie beside him and am jealous of the sleep that takes
him from my sight. The morning comes and sets my heart to beating
at the thought that one more long, sweet day has come to me in
which to guard, and love, and cherish him.

Your Happy Wife

28

It has been a wonderful day. Your son has had his first reception. It is just one moon ago since I found him lying by my side,
and now we have had the feast of the shaving of the head. All our
friends came, they brought him beautiful presents. Chih-lo gave a
cap with all the gods upon the front and long red tassels to hang
down each ear. Li-ti gave him shoes that she herself had embroidered, with a cat's face on the toes and the ears and whiskers out-
standing. They will make him careful of his step and surefooted as
the cat. Mah-li gave him a most wonderful silver box to hang
around his neck and in which I will keep his amulets. There were
many things that I will not take the time to tell you. I am sorry to

say that your son behaved
himself unseemly. He screamed
and kicked as the barber
shaved his tiny head. I was
much distressed, but they tell
me it is a sign that he will
grow to be a valiant man.

I gave a feast, and such a
feast! It will be remembered
for many moons. Even your
Honorable Mother said I
showed the knowledge of what
was due my guests upon so
great an occasion. We also
gave to him his milk name.
It is Ten Thousand Spring-
times, as he came at blossom
time; but I call him that only
within my heart, as I do not
wish the jealous gods to hear.
When I speak of him, I say
"The Stupid One," "The
Late-Born," so they will think
I do not care for him and will
not covet me my treasure.

I am tired; it has been a
happy day. The gods are
good to

Kwei-li

My Dear One,

Another marriage within our compound. Do you remember the servant Cho-to, who came to us soon after I became your bride? She will soon marry a man in the village of Soong-tong, and she is very happy. She has not seen him, of course, but her mother says he is good and honest and will make her a suitable husband. I talked to her quite seriously, as my age and many moons of marriage allow me. I told her that only by practicing modesty, humility, and gentleness could she walk safely on the path that leads to being the mother of sons.

To be the mother of sons is not always a happiness. Ling-ti, the shoemaker, was here this morning, and he was in great distress. His baby, three months old, died with a fever and he had no money to pay for burial. This morning he arose early, before the mother awakened, and took it to the baby tower outside the city. It is lying there now, with all the other little children whose parents were too poor to give them proper burial. It made a quick, sad hurt within me, and I went quickly to find my baby. You will not laugh, but I have pierced his right ear and put a ring therein, so the gods will think he is a girl and not desire him.

I hear your son.

Your Wife

My Dear One,

There has been great talk of evil eyes. Not that I believe the servants' tales; but—your Honorable Mother, Li-ti, and your wife have
been to the Holy Man who dwells underneath the Great Magnolia
tree near the street of the Leaning Willow. He lives alone within a
little house of matting, and has acquired great merit by his virtuous
acts. He wears around his unbound hair a band of metal that is the
outward sign of his great holiness. He lives alone in peace and with
untroubled mind. In his great wisdom he has learned that peace is
the end and aim of life; not triumph, success, or riches, but that the
greatest gift from all the gods is peace. I purchased from him an
amulet for my "Stupid One," my treasure, as someone might come
within our courtyard and cast his eye upon our child with bad
intent.

Come to me, my husband. Tell me you are coming. You will find
me standing in the outer archway with your son within my arms. I
long for you.

Your Wife

30

My days are filled with happiness. I go out on the terrace and look far down the hillside, which is covered with azaleas, pink and orange and mauve. I hold my son and say, "Look, your father will come to us from the city yonder. Our eyes of love will see him from far away, there by the willow-pattern teahouse. He will come nearer—nearer—and we will not hear the beat of his bearers' feet upon the pathway because of the beating of our hearts." He smiles at me; he understands. He is so wonderful, your son. I would "string the sunbeams for his necklace or draw down the moon with cords to canopy his bed."

Come back and see your son.

Kwei-li

My Dear One,

Your letter has come saying you will be here soon. It came on the day I went to the temple to make my offering of thanks for the gift of our son.

I put on my richest gown, the blue one with the embroidery of gold. I dressed my hair with jessamine flowers, and wore all the jewels you have given me. My boy was in his red jacket, his mauve trousers, his purple shoes, and his cap with the many gods. When I was seated in the chair he was placed in my lap, and a man was sent ahead with cash to give the beggars, because I wished all the world to be happy on this, my day of rejoicing.

My bearers carried me to the very steps of the throne on which Kwan-yin was seated. I made my obeisance, I lit the large red candles and placed them before the Goddess of Heaven. Then I took our son before the Buddha, the Name, the Lord of Light, the All-Powerful, and touched his head three times to the mat, to show that he would be a faithful follower and learn to keep the law.

We went home by the valley road, and my heart kept beating in tune to the pat-pat of the bearers' feet on the pathway. It was all so beautiful. The trailing vines on the mountainside, the ferns in the cool dark places, the rich green leaves of the mulberry trees, the farmers in the paddy fields, all seemed filled with the joy of life. And I, Kwei-li, going along in my chair with my son on my knee, was the happiest of them all. The gods have given me everything; they have nothing more to bestow. I am glad I have gone to the mountainside each day to thank them for their gifts.

The gods are good, my loved one, they are good to your

Kwei-li

I am alone on the mountaintop. I have gone the pathway the last time to lay my offering at the feet of Kwan-yin. She does not hear my voice. There is no Goddess of Mercy. She is a thing of gold and wood, and she has mocked my despair, has laughed at the heart that is within me, which is alive and full of anguish such as she has never known.

My son, my man-child is dead. The life has gone from his body, the breath from his lips. I have held him all the night close to my heart and it does not give him warmth. They have taken him from me and told me he has gone to the gods. There are no gods. There are no gods. I am alone.

34   He had your eyes—he was like you. You will never know your son and mine, my Springtime. Why could they not have left your son for you to see? He was so strong and beautiful, my firstborn.

35   Do not chide me. I cannot write. What do I do? I do not know. I lie long hours and watch the tiny motes that live within the sun's bright golden rays, and say, "Why could I not exchange my womanhood, which hopes and loves and sorrows, for one of those small dancing spots within the sunbeams? At least they do not feel."

At night sleep does not touch my eyelids. I lie upon the terrace. I will not go within my chamber, where there is gloom and darkness. I watch the stars, a silver, mocking throng, that twinkle at me coldly, and then I see the moon slowly mount her pathway of the skies. The noises of the night come to me softly, as if they knew my sorrow, and the croaking frogs and the crickets that find lodging by the lotus pool seem to feel my loneliness with me, so plaintive is their cry.

I feel the dawn will never come, as if it were dead or slumbered; but when at last he comes, I watch him touch the hillside, trees, and temples with soft gray fingers, and bring to me a beauty one does not see by day. The night winds pass with sighs among the pine trees, and in passing give a loving touch to bells upon pagodas that bring their faint music to me. The dawn is not the golden door of happiness. It only means another day has come and I must smile and talk and live as if my heart were here.

Oh, man of mine, if but your dream touch would come and bid me slumber, I would obey.

Your Wife

They have put a baby in my arms, a child found on the towpath, a beggar child. I felt I could not place another head where our dear boy had lain, and I sat stiff and still, and tried to push away the little body pressing close against me; but at touch of baby mouth and fingers, springs that were dead seemed stirring in my heart again. At last I could not bear it, and I leaned my face against her head and crooned His lullaby:

The gods on the rooftree guard pigeons from harm
And my little pigeon is safe in my arms.

I cannot tell you more. My heart is breaking.

36

I have given this stranger-child, this child left to die upon the towpath, the clothes that were our son's. She was cold, and your Mother came to me so gently and said, "Kwei-li, have you no clothing for the child that was found by the servants?" I saw her meaning, and I said, "Would you have me put the clothing over which I have wept, and which is now carefully laid away in the camphor-wood box, upon this child?" She said—and you would know your Mother's voice, her bitter words are only as the rough shell of the lichee nut that covers the sweet meat hidden within—she said, "Why not, dear one? This one needs them, and the hours you pass with them are only filled with saddened memories." I said to her, "This child is a girl, a beggar's child. I will not give to her the clothing of my son. Each time I looked upon her it would be a knife plunged in my heart." She said to me, "Kwei-li, you are not a child, you are a woman. Of what worth is that clothing lying in that box of camphor wood? Does it bring back your son? Someday you will open it, and there will be nothing but dust, which will reproach you. Get them and give them to this child who has come to us out of the night."

I went to the box and opened it, and they lay there, the little things that had touched his tiny body. I gave them, the trousers of purple, the jackets of red, the embroidered shoes, the caps with the many Buddhas. I gave them all to the beggar child.

I am,
Your Wife

I am reproached because I will not go to the temple. It is filled with the sounds of chanting, which come to me faintly as I lie upon the terrace. There are women there, happy women, with their babies in their arms, while mine are empty. There are others there in sorrow, laying their offerings at the feet of Kwan-yin. They do not know that she does not feel, nor care, for womankind. She sits upon her lotus throne and laughs at mothers in despair. How can she feel, how can she know, that thing of gilded wood and plaster?

I stay upon my terrace, I live alone within my court of silent dreams. For me there are no gods.

They have brought to me from the marketplace a book of a new god. I would not read it. I said, "There are too many gods—why add a new one? I have no candles or incense to lay before an image." But—I read and saw within its pages that He gave rest and love and peace. Peace—what the holy man desired, the end of all things—peace. And I, I do not want to lose the gift of memory; I want remembrance, but I want it without pain.

The cherry blossoms have bloomed and passed away. They lingered but a moment's space, and, like my dream of spring, they died. But, passing, they have left behind the knowledge that we'll see them once again. There must be something, *somewhere,* to speak to despairing mothers and say, "Weep not! You will see your own again."

I do not want a god of temples. I have cried my prayers to Kwan-yin, and they have come back to me like echoes from a deadened wall. I want a god to come to me at nighttime, when I am lying lonely, wide-eyed, staring into darkness, with all my body aching for the touch of tiny hands. I want that god who says, "I give you Peace," to stand close to my pillow and touch my wearied eyelids and bring me rest.

I have been dead—enclosed within a tomb of sorrow and despair; but now, at words dimly understood, a faint new life seems stirring deep within me. A voice that says, "Come unto Me all ye who are weary and heavy-laden, and I will give thee rest." My longing soul cries out, "Oh, great and unknown God, give *me* this rest!" I am alone, a woman, helpless, stretching out my arms in darkness, but into my world of gloom has come a faint dim star, a star of hope that says to me, "There *is* a God."

P
a
r
t

T
w
o

My Dear Mother,

Your son has received his appointment as governor of this province, and we are at last settled in this new and strange abode. We are most proud of the words pronounced by His Excellency Yuan when giving him his power of office. He said:

> You, Liu, are an example of that higher patriotism rarely met with in official life, which recognizes its duty to its government, a duty too often forgotten by the members of a great family such as that of which you are the honored head, in the obligation of the clan and the desire to use power for personal advantage. Your personal record has been without stain; and especially your work among the foreigners dwelling in our land has been accom-

1

plished with tact and discretion. I am sending you to Shanghai, which is the most difficult post in the republic because of its involved affairs with the foreign nations, knowing that the interests of the republic will always be safe in your hands.

I write you this because I know your mother-heart will rejoice that our president shows such confidence in your son, and that his many years of service to his country have been appreciated.

Shanghai truly is a difficult place at present. There are fifteen nationalities here represented by their consuls, and they are all watching China and each other with jealous eyes, each nation fearing that another will obtain some slight advantage in the present unsettled state of our country. The town is filled with adventurers, both European and Chinese, who are waiting anxiously to see what attitude the new governor takes in regard to the many projects in which they are interested. My husband says nothing and allows them all to wonder. It is better for them, because, like all schemers, if they had nothing to give them anxious nights and troubled dreams, they would not be happy.

We found the *Yamen* not suitable for our large household, as it did not lend itself readily to the reception of foreigners and the innovations and new customs that seem to be necessary for the fulfillment of the duties of a Chinese official under this new order. As your son was selected governor of this province because of his knowledge of foreign lands and customs, it is necessary for him to live, partly at least, the life of a European; but let me assure you that, so far as I am concerned, and so far as I can influence it, our life behind the screens will always be purely Chinese, and the old, unchanged customs that I love will rule my household. I will surrender no more than necessary to this new tide of Westernism that seems to be sweeping our China from its moorings. But—I must not dwell too much upon that theme, though it is a subject on which I can wax most eloquent, and I know your desire to hear of this house, which would seem so ugly to your eyes.

There are no quiet courtyards, no curving roofs, no softly shaded windows of shell, no rounded archways; but all is square and glaring and imposing, seeming to look coldly from its staring glass windows at the stranger within its gates. It says loudly, "I am rich; it cost many thousands of *taels* to make my ugliness." For me, it is indeed a "foreign" house. Yet I will have justice within my heart and tell you that there is much that we might copy with advantage. In place of floors of wide plain boards, and walls of wood with great wide cracks covered with embroideries and rugs, as in the Chinese homes, the floors are made of tiny boards polished until they glisten like the sides of the boats of the teahouse girls, and the walls are plaster, covered, as in our rooms of reception, with silk and satin, and the chairs and couches have silken tapestry to match. This furniture, strange to me, is a great care, as I do not understand its uses; it seems most stiff and formal. I hope someday to know a foreign woman on terms of friendship, and I will ask her to touch the room with her hands of knowledge, and bring each piece into more friendly companionship with its neighbor. Now chairs look coldly at tables, as if to say, "You are an intruder!" and it chills me. This house is much more simple than our homes, because of the many modern instruments that make the work less heavy and allow it to be done by few instead of many, as is our way. It is not necessary to have a man attend solely to the lighting of the lamps. Upon the wall is placed a magic button that, touched even by the hand of ignorance, floods the room with the light of many suns. We see no more the water carrier with his two great wooden buckets swinging from the bamboo as he comes from the river or canal to pour the water into the great *kangs* standing by the kitchen door. Nor do we need to put the powder in it to make it clear and wholesome. That is all done by men we do not see, and they call it "sanitation." The cook needs only to turn a small brass handle, and the water comes forth as from a distant spring. It reminds me of the man who came to my father, when he was governor of Wuseh, and wished to install a most unheard-of machine to bring water to the city from the lake upon the hillside. My father listened most respectfully to the long and stupid explanation, and looked at the clear water the foreign man produced to show what could be done, then, shaking his head, said, "Perhaps that water is more healthful, as you say, but it is to me too clear and white. It has no body, and I fear has not the strength of the water from our canals."

Another thing we do not hear is the rattle of the watchman as he makes his rounds at night, and I miss it. In far Szechwan, on many nights when sleep was distant, I would lie and listen as he struck upon his piece of hollow bamboo telling me that all was well within our compound. Now the city has police that stand outside the gateway. Many are men from India—big black men, with fierce black beards and burning eyes. Our people hate them, and they have good cause. They are most cruel, and ill-treat all who come within their power. But we must tread with catlike steps, as they are employed by the English, who protect them at all times. They are the private army of that nation here within our city, and at every chance their numbers are constantly increased. I do not understand this question of police. There are in thousands of our cities and villages no police, no soldiers, yet there is less lawlessness and vice in a dozen purely Chinese cities than in this great mongrel town that spends many tens of thousands of *taels* each year upon these guardians of the peo-

ple's peace. It seems to me that this should tell the world that the
force of China is not a physical force, but the force of the law-
abiding instinct of a happy common people, who, although living on
the verge of misery and great hunger, live upright lives and do not
try to break their country's laws.

There is a garden within our walls, but not a garden of winding
pathways and tiny bridges leading over lotus ponds, nor are there
small mounds of rocks with here and there a tiny god or temple
peeping from some hidden grotto. All is flat, with long bare
stretches of green grass over which are nets, by which my children
play a game called tennis. This game is foolish, in my eyes, and con-
sists of much jumping and useless waste of strength, but the English
play it, and of course the modern Chinese boy must imitate them. I
have made one rule: My daughters shall not play the game. It seems
to me most shameful to see a woman run madly, with great boorish
strides, in front of men and boys. My daughters pout and say it is
played by all the girls in school, and that it makes them strong and
well; but I am firm. I have conceded many things, but this to me is
vulgar and unseemly.

Need I tell you, Mother of mine, that I am a stranger in this
great city, that my heart calls for the hills and the mountainside with
its ferns and blossoms? Yesterday at the hour of twilight I drove to
the country in the motor (a new form of carrying chair that you
would not understand — or like) and I stopped by a field of flowering mustard. The scent brought remembrance to my heart, and tears
flowed from beneath my eyelids. The delicate yellow blossoms
seemed to speak to me from their golden throats, and I yearned to
hold within my arms all this beauty of the earth flowering beneath
my feet. We stayed until the darkness came, and up to the blue
night rose from all the fields "that great soft, bubbling chorus which

seems the very voice of the earth itself—
the chant of the frogs." When we turned
back and saw the vulgar houses, with
straight red tops and piercing chimneys, I
shut my eyes and in a vision saw the
blue-gray houses with their curved
up-tilted roofs nestling among the groves
of bamboo, and I felt that if it were my
misfortune to spend many moons in this
great alien city, my heart would break
with longing for the beautiful home I love.

I felt sympathy with Kang Tang-li, of
my father's province, who heard of a new
god in Anhui. He had eaten bitter sorrow
and he felt that the old gods had forgotten him and did not hear his call, so
he walked two long days' journey to find
this new god who gave joy and peace to
those who came to him. He arrived at
evening time, the sun was setting in a lake
of gold, but even with its glory it could
not change the ugly square-built temple,
with no curves or grace to mark it as a
dwelling place of the gods. Kang walked
slowly around this temple, looked long at
its staring windows and its tall and ugly
spire upon the rooftree, which seemed to
force its way into the kindly dark blue
sky; then, saddened, sick at heart, he
turned homeward, saying deep within him

K
w
e
i
.
l
i

that no god whom he could revere would choose a house so lacking in all beauty for a dwelling place.

Is this a long and tiresome letter, my Honorable Mother? But you are far away, and in your sheltered walls yearn to know what has come to us, your children, in this new and foreign life. It is indeed a new life for me, and I can hardly grasp its meaning. They are trying hard to force us to change our old quiet and peace for the rush and worry of the Western world, and I fear I am too old and settled for such sudden changes.

Tell Mah-li's daughter that I will send her news of the latest fashions, and tell Li-ti that the hair is dressed quite differently here. I will write her more about it and send her the new ornaments. They are not so pretty, in my eyes, nor are the gowns so graceful, but I will send her patterns that she may choose.

We all give you our greetings and touch your hand with love.

Kwei-li

My Dear Mother,

I have not written you for so long, as my days have been filled with strange, new duties. The wives of the foreign officials have called upon me, as that appears to be their custom. It seems to me quite useless and a waste of time; but they come, and I must return the calls. I do not understand why the consuls cannot transact their business with the governor without trying to peer into his inner life.

To us a man's official life and that which lies within his women's courtyard are as separate as two pathways that never meet.

The foreign woman comes and sits upon the edge of her chair in great discomfort, vainly searching for a subject upon which we may have a common bond. I sit upon the edge of the chair from necessity, as these chairs are far too high for me, and my tiny feet hang helplessly in the air. Although the chairs are not so high or so straight and stiff as are our seats of honor, they have no footstools, and no small tables on which to lean the arm. You would laugh at our poor feeble efforts to be agreeable one to the other. Our conversation is as foolish and as useless as would be the using of a paper lantern for the rice mill. With all desire to be courteous and to put her at ease, I ask about her children, the health of her honorable mother, and the state of her household. I do not ask her age, as I have learned that, contrary to our usage, it is a question not considered quite auspicious, and often causes the flush of great embarrassment to rise to the cheek of a guest. Often she answers in "pidgin" English, a kind of baby talk that is used when addressing servants. These foreign women have rarely seen a Chinese lady, and they are surprised that I speak English; often I have been obliged to explain that when I found that my husband's office brought him close to foreigners, and that my sons and daughters were learning the new education in which it is necessary to know other than their mother tongue, I would not be left behind within closed doors, so I too learned of English and of French enough to read and speak. I am to them a curiosity. It has not been correct in former times to know a Chinese lady socially; and to these ladies, with their society, their calls, their dinners, and their games of cards, we within the courtyards are people from another world. They think that Chinese women are and always have been closely prisoned slaves of their husbands, idle and ignorant and soulless, with no thoughts above their petty household cares and the strange heathen gods they worship.

Of course, these foreign women do not say these things in words, but their looks are most expressive, and I understand. I serve them tea and cake, of which they take most sparingly, and when the proper time has come they rise, trying not to look relieved that their martyrdom is over. I conduct them to the doorway, or, if the woman is the wife of a great official, to the outer entrance. Then I return to my own rooms amidst the things I understand; and I fear, *I fear*, Mother of mine, that I gossip with my household upon the ways and dress and manners of these queer people from distant lands.

I have been asked to join a society of European and Chinese ladies for the purpose of becoming acquainted with one another, but I do not think that I will do so. I believe it impossible for the woman of the West to form an alliance with the woman of the East that will be deep rooted. The thoughts within our hearts are different, as are our points of view. We do not see the world through the same eyes. The foreign woman has children like myself, but their ambitions and ideals for them are different. She has a home and a husband, but my training and my instincts give my home and my husband a different place in life than that which she gives to those of her household. To me the words marriage, friendship, home have deeper meanings than are attached to them by a people who live in hotels and public eating places, and who are continually in the homes of others. They have no sanctity of the life within; there are no shrines set apart for the family union, and the worship of the spirits of their ancestors. I cannot well explain to you the something intangible, the thick gray mist that is always there to put its bar across the open door of friendship between the woman of the Occident and those of Oriental blood.

I would ask of you a favor. I wish that you would search my rooms and find the clothing not needed by your women. My house is full and overflowing. I had no idea we had so many poor relations. The poor relation and the cousin of our cousin's cousin have come to claim their kinship. Your son will give no one official position nor allow them money from the public funds; but they must have clothing and rice, and I provide it. I sometimes feel, when looking into the empty rice bin, that I sympathize with His Excellency Li Hung-chang who built a great house here, far from his home province. When asked why, unlike the Chinese custom, he built so far from kith and kin, he answered, "You have placed the finger upon the pulse beat the first instant. I built it far away, hoping that all the relatives of my relatives who find themselves in need might not find the money wherewith to buy a ticket in order to come and live beneath my rooftree." (With us, they do not wait for tickets; they have strong, willing feet.) I am afraid that His Excellency, although of the old China that I love, was touched with this new spirit of "each member for himself" that has come upon this country.

It is the good of the one instead of the whole, as in the former times, and there is much that can be said upon both sides. The family should always stand for the members of the clan in the great crises of their lives, and help to care for them in days of poverty and old age. It is not just that one should prosper while others of the same blood starve; yet it is not just that one should provide for those unwilling to help themselves. I can look back with eyes of greater knowledge to our home, and I fear that there are many eating from the bowl of charity who might be working and self-respecting if they were not members of the great family Liu, and so entitled to your help.

It is the hour for driving with the children. We all are yours and think of you each day.

Kwei-li

My Mother,

I have such great news to tell you that I hardly know where to begin. But, first, I will astonish you—Ting-fang is home! Yes, I can hear you say, "Hi yah!" and I said it many times when, the evening before last, after your son and the men of the household had finished the evening meal, and I and the women were preparing to eat our rice, we saw a darkness in the archway, and standing there was my son. Not one of us spoke a word; we were as if turned to stone; as we thought of him as in far-off America, studying at the college of Yale. But here he stood in real life, smiling at our astonishment. He slowly looked at us all, then went to his father and saluted him respectfully, came and bowed before me, then took me in his arms in a most disrespectful manner and squeezed me together so hard he nearly broke my bones. I was so frightened and so pleased that of course I could only cry and cling to this great boy of mine whom I had not seen for six long years. I held him away from me and looked long into his face. He is a man now, twenty-one years old, a big, strong man, taller than his father. I can hardly reach his shoulder. He is straight and slender, and looks alien in his foreign dress, yet when I looked into his eyes I knew it was mine own come to me again.

No one knows how all my dreams followed this bird that left the nest. No one knows how long the nights seemed when sleep would not come to my eyes and I wondered what would happen to my boy in that far-off land, a strange land with strange, unloving people, who would not care to put him on the pathway when he strayed. You remember how I battled with his father in regard to sending him to England to commence his foreign education. I said, "Is not four years of college in America enough? Why four years' separation to go to that college? He will go from me a boy and return a man. I will lose my son." But his father firmly said that the English public schools gave the groundwork for a useful life. He must form his

code of honor and his character upon the rules laid down for centuries by the English, and then go to America for the education of the intellect, to learn to apply the lessons learned in England. He did not want his son to be all for present success, as the American, or to be all for tradition, as is the Englishman, but he thought the two might find a happy meeting place in a mind not yet well formed.

But thoughts of learning did not assuage the pain in my mother-heart. I had heard of dreadful things happening to our Chinese boys who are sent abroad to get a Western knowledge. Often they marry strange women who have no place in our life if they return to China, and who are ostracized by their own race for marrying a Chinese. Neither side can be

blamed — certainly not our boys. They go there alone, often with little money. They live in houses where they are offered food and
lodging at the cheapest price. They are not in a position to meet
women of their own class, and being boys they crave the society of
girls. Perhaps the daughter of the woman who keeps the lodging
house speaks to them kindly, talks to them in the evening when they
have no place to go except a lonely, ugly room; or the girl in the
shop where they buy their clothing smiles as she wraps their packages for them. Such attentions would be passed by without a
thought at ordinary times, but now notice means much to a heart
that is trying hard to stifle its loneliness and sorrow, struggling to
learn the knowledge of the West in an unknown tongue; in lieu of
mother, sister, or sweetheart of his own land, the boy is insensibly
drawn into a net that tightens about him, until he takes the fatal
step and brings back to his mother a woman of another race.

One sorrows for the girl, whatever may be her station, as she
does not realize that there is no place for her in all the old land of
China. She will be scorned by those of foreign birth, and she can
never become one of us. Do you remember the wife of Wang, the
secretary of the embassy at London? He was most successful and
was given swift promotions until he married the English lady, whose
father was a tutor at one of the great colleges. It angered Her Majesty and he was recalled and given the small post of secretary to the
Taotai of our city. The poor foreign wife died alone within her
Chinese home, into which no friend had entered to bid her welcome.
Some say that after many moons of solitude and loneliness she
drank the strong drink of her country to drown her sorrow. Perhaps
it was a bridge on which she crossed to a land filled with the memories of the past that brought her solace in her time of desolation.

But I have wandered, Mother of mine; my mind has taken me to

England, America, to Chinese men with foreign wives, and now I will return and tell you of your own again, and of my son who has returned to me. When at last the gods gave us our breath, we asked the many questions that came to us like a river that has broken all its bounds. Your son, the father of Ting-fang, was more than angry—he was white with wrath, and demanded to know what Ting-fang was doing here when he should have been at school. My son said, and I admired the way he spoke up boldly to his father, "Father, I read each day of the progress of the revolution, of the new China that was being formed, and I could not stay on and study books while I might be helping here." His father said, "Your duty was to stay where I, your father, put you!" Ting-fang answered, "You could not have sat still and studied of ancient Greece and Rome while your country was fighting for its life"; and then he added, most unfilially, "I notice you are not staying in Szechwan, but are here in Shanghai, in the center of things. I am your son; I do not like to sit quietly by the road and watch the world pass by; I want to help make that world, the same as you."

His father talked long and bitterly, and the boy was saddened. I crept silently to him and placed my hand on his. It was all I could do for the moment, as it would not be seemly for me to take his part against his father, but—I talked to your son, my husband, when we were alone within our chamber.

The storm has passed. His father refused to make Ting-fang a secretary, as he says the time is past when officials fill their *Yamens* with their relatives and friends. I think that as the days go on, he will relent, as in these troubled times a high official cannot be sure of the loyalty of the men who eat his rice, and he can rely upon his son. A Liu was never known to be disloyal.

There is too much agitation here. The officials try to ignore it as much as possible, believing that muddy water is often made clear if allowed to stand still. Yet they must be ready to act quickly, as speedily as one springs up when a serpent is creeping into the lap, because now the serpent of treachery and ingratitude is in every household. These secret plottings, like the weeds that thrust their roots deep into the rice fields, cannot be taken out without bringing with them some grain, and many an innocent family is now suffering for the hotheadedness of its youth.

I sometimes think that I agree with the wise governor of the olden time whose motto was to empty the minds of the people and fill their stomachs, weaken their wills, and strengthen their bones. When times were troubled he opened the government granaries and the crowds were satisfied.

But the people are different now; they have too much knowledge. New ambitions have been stirred; new wants created; a new spirit is abroad and, with mighty power, it is overturning and recasting the old forms and deeply rooted customs. China is moving, and—we of the old school think—too quickly. She is going at a bound from the dim light of the bean-oil brazier to the dazzling brilliance of the electric light; from the leisured slowness of the wheelbarrow pushed by the patient coolie to the speed of the modern motor car; from the practice of the seller of herbs to the science of the modern doctor. We all feel that new China is at a great turning point because she is just starting out on her journey, which may last many centuries, or which may see its final struggle tomorrow. It is of great importance that the right direction be taken at first. A wrong turn at the beginning, and the true pathway may never be found. So much depends upon her leaders, on men like Yuan, Wu, and your son, my husband: the men who point out the road to those who will follow as wild foul follow their leader. The Chinese people are keen to note disinterestedness, and if these men who have risen up show that they have the good of the people at heart much may be done. If they have the corrupt heart of many of the old-time officials, China will remain as before, so far as the great mass of her men are concerned.

I hear the children coming from their school, so I will say good-bye for a time. Ting-fang sends his most respectful love, and all my household join in sending you good wishes.

Kwei-li

4

My Dear Mother,

Do you remember Liang Tai-tai, the daughter of the Princess Tseng, your old friend of Pau-chau? You remember we used to laugh at the pride of Liang in regard to her mother's clan, and her care in speaking of her father who was only a small official in the governor's *Yamen.* You were wont to say that she reminded you of the mule that, when asked who was his father, answered, "The horse is my maternal uncle." She comes to see me often, and she worries me with her piety; she is quite mad upon the subject of the gods. I often feel that I am wrong to be so lacking in sympathy with her religious longings; but I hate extremes. "Extreme straightness is as bad as crookedness, and extreme cleverness as bad as folly." She is ever asking me if I do not desire, above all things, the life of the higher road—whatever that may mean. I tell her that I do not know. I would not be rare, like jade, or common, like stone; just medium. Anyway, my days are far too full to think about any other road than the one I must tread each day in the fulfillment of the duties the gods have given me.

Some people seem to be irreverently familiar with the gods, and to be forever praying. If they would only be a little more human and perform the daily work that lies before them (Liang's son is the main support of the Golden Lotus Teahouse) they might let prayer alone awhile without ceasing to enjoy the protection of the gods. It is dangerous to overload oneself with piety, as the sword that is polished to excess is sometimes polished away. And there is another side that Liang should remember, her husband not having riches in abundance: that the rays of the gods love the rays of gold.

But today she came to me with her rice bowl overflowing with her sorrows. Her son has returned from the foreign lands with the new education from which she hoped so much, but it seems he has acquired knowledge of the vices of the foreigner to add to those of the Chinese. He did not stay long enough to lose touch with the people and the customs of his country. He forgets that he is not an American even with his foreign education; he is still an Oriental and he comes back to an Oriental land, a land tied down by tradition and custom, and he cannot adapt himself. He tries instead to adapt China to his half-Europeanized way of thought, and he has failed. He has become what my husband calls an agitator, a teahouse orator, and he sees nothing but wrong in his people. There is no place in life for him, and he sits at night in public places, stirring foolish boys to deeds of treason and violence. Another thing, he has learned to drink foreign wines, and the mixture is not good. They will not blend with Chinese wine, any more than the two civilizations will come together as one.

Why did the gods make the first draught of wine to curse the race of men, to make blind the reason, to make angels into devils, and to leave a lasting curse on all who touch it? "It is a cataract that carries havoc with it in a road of mire where he who falls may never rise again." It seems to me that he who drinks the wine of both lands allows it to become a ring that leads him to the Land of Nothing, and ends as did my friend's son, with the small round ball of sleep that grows within the poppy. One morning's light when he looked into his own face and saw the marks that life was leaving, he saw no way except the Bridge of Death; but he was not successful.

His mother brought him to me, as he has always liked me, and is a friend (for which I sorrow) of my son. I talked to him alone within an inner chamber, and tried to show him the error of his way. I quoted to him the words spoken to another foolish youth who tried to force the gates of Heaven: "My son, you are enmeshed within this world's ways, and have not cared to wonder where the stream would carry you in coming days. If you scorn mere human duties, as a worn sandal cast aside, you are no man but stock-stone born, lost in a selfish senseless pride. If you could mount Heaven's high plain, then your own will might be your guide, but your needs must dwell here on earth. You can well see that you are not wanted in the Halls of Heaven; so turn to things near; turn to your earthly home and try to do your duty here. You must control yourself, there is no escape through the Eastern Gateway for the necessity of self-conquest."

He wept and gave me many promises; and I showed him that I believed him, and saw his worth. But—we think it wiser to send him far away from his companions, who only seek to drag him down. Your son will give to him a letter and ask the Prefect of Canton to give him work at our expense.

I felt it better that Liang Tai-tai should not be alone with her son for several hours, as her tongue is bitter and reproaches come easily to angry lips. So I took her with me to the garden of a friend outside the city. It was the Dragon Boat Festival, when all the world goes riverward to send their lighted boats upon the waters searching for the soul of the great poet who drowned himself in the olden time, and whose body the jealous Water God took to himself and it was nevermore found. Do you remember how we told the story to the children when the family was all with you—oh, it seems many moons ago.

The garden of my friend was most beautiful, and we seemed within a world apart. The way was through high woods and over long green plots of grass and around queer rocks; there were flowers with stories in their hearts, and trees who held the spirits of the air close beneath their ragged covering. Pigeons called softly to their mates, and doves cooed and sobbed as they nestled one to the other. We showed the children the filial young crow who, when his parents are old and helpless, feeds them in return for their care when he was young; and we pointed out the young dove sitting three branches lower on the tree than do his parents, so deep is his respect.

When the western sky was like a golden curtain, we went to the canal, where the children set their tiny boats afloat, each with its lighted lantern. The wind cried softly through the bamboo trees and

filled the sails of these small barks, whose lights flashed brightly from the waters as if the Spirits of the River laughed with joy.

We returned home, happy, tired, but with new heart to start the morrow's work.

Your daughter,
Kwei-li

My Dear Mother,

We are in the midst of a most perplexing problem, and one that is hard for us to cope with, as it is so utterly new. My children seem to have formed an alliance amongst themselves in opposition to the wishes of their parents on all subjects touching the customs and traditions of the family. My son, you remember, was betrothed in childhood to the daughter of his father's friend, the governor of Chih-li. He is a man now, and should fulfill that most solemn obligation that we, his parents, laid upon him—and he refuses. I can see you sit back aghast at his lack of filial spirit; and I, too, am aghast. I cannot understand this generation; I'm afraid that I cannot understand these, my children. My boy insists that he will marry a girl of his own choice, a girl with a foreign education like his own. We have remonstrated, we have urged, we have commanded, and now at last a compromise has been effected. We have agreed that when she comes to us, teachers shall be brought to the house and she shall be taught the new learning. Along with the duties of wife she shall see the new life around her and from it take what is best for her to know.

I can understand his desire to have a wife with whom he may talk of the things of common interest to them both, a wife who can share with him, at least in part, the life beyond the women's court-yard. I remember how I felt when your son returned from foreign lands, filled with new sights, new thoughts in which I could not share. I had been sitting quietly behind closed doors, and I felt that I could not help in this new vision that had come to him. I could speak to only one side of his life, when I wished to speak to all; but I studied, I learned, and, as far as it is possible for a Chinese woman, I have made my steps agree with those of my husband, and we march close, side by side.

My son would like his wife to be placed in a school, the school from which my daughter has just graduated; but I will not allow it. I am not in favor of such schools for our girls. It has made of Wan-li a half-trained Western woman, who finds music in the piano instead of the lute, who quotes from Shelley, and Wordsworth, in-stead of from the Chinese classics, who thinks embroidery work for servants, and the ordering of her household a thing beneath her great mental status.

I, of course, wish her to marry at once; as to me that is the holi-est desire of woman—to marry and give men-children to the world; but it seems the word "marry" has opened the door to floods of talk to which I can only listen in silent amazement. I never before had realized that I have the honor of bearing children with such tongues of eloquence; and I fully understand that I belong to the past, a very ancient past—the Mings, from what I hear, are my contemporaries. And all these words are poured upon me to try to persuade me to allow Wan-li to become a doctor. Can you imagine it? A *daughter* of the house of Liu a *doctor*! From whence has she received these unseemly ideas except in this foreign school that teaches the equality of the sexes to such an extent that our daughters want to compete with men in their professions! I am not so much of the past as my daughter seems to think; for I believe, within certain bounds, in the social freedom of our women: but why commercial freedom?

For centuries untold, men have been able to support their wives; why enter the marketplaces? Is it not enough that they take care of the home, that they train the children and fulfill the duties of the life in which the gods place women? My daughter is not ugly, she is most beautiful; yet she says she will not marry. I tell her that when her eyes are opened to the loved one, they will be closed to all the world beside, and this desire to enter the great world of turmoil and strife will flee like dewdrops before the summer's dawn. I also quoted her what I told Chih-peh many moons ago, when he refused to marry the wife you had chosen for him: "Man attains not by himself, nor woman by herself, but like the one-winged birds of the ancient legend, they must rise together."

My daughter tossed her head and answered me that those were doubtless words of great wisdom, but they were written by a man long dead, and it did not affect her ideas upon the subject of *her* marriage.

We dare not insist, for we find, to our horror, that she has joined a band of girls who have made a vow, writing it with their blood, that—rather than become wives to husbands not of their own choice—they will cross the River of Death. Fifteen girls, all friends of my daughter, and all of whom have been studying the new education for women, have joined this sisterhood; and we, their mothers, are in despair. What can we do? Shall we insist that they return to the old regime and learn nothing but embroidery? Why can they not take what is best for Eastern woman from the learning of the West, as the bee selects honey from each flower, and leave the rest? It takes centuries of training to change the habits and thoughts of a nation. It cannot be done at once; our girls have not the foundation on which to build. Our womanhood has been trained by centuries of caressing care to look as lovely as nature allows, to learn obedience to father as a child, to husband as a wife, and to children when age comes with his frosty fingers.

Yet we all know that the last is a theory only to be read in books. Where is there one so autocratic in her own home as a Chinese mother? She lives within its four walls, but there she is supreme. Her sons obey her even when their hair is touched with silver. Did not your son have to ask your leave before he would decide that he could go with His Highness to the foreign lands? Did he not say frankly that he must consult his mother, and was he not honored and given permission to come to his home to have your blessing? Do you remember when Yuan was appointed secretary to the embassy in London, and declined the honor because his mother was old and did not wish her only son to journey overseas; he gave up willingly and cheerfully the one great opportunity of his life rather than bring sorrow to the one who bore him.

A similar case came to our ears but a few days ago. Some priests of a foreign mission came to my husband and wished him to intercede as governor and command the *Taotai* of Soochow to sell to them a piece of land on which to erect a temple of their faith. When the *Taotai* was asked why he was so persistent in his refusal, he told the governor that the temple where his mother worshiped was in a direct line with the proposed new foreign house of worship. His mother feared that a spire would be placed upon its rooftree that would intercept the good spirits of the air and keep them from bringing the blessings from the temple directly to her family rooftree. My husband tried to persuade him that the superstitions of a woman long in years should not stand in the way of a possible quarrel with men of a foreign power, but the *Taotai* only shrugged his shoulders and said, "What can I do? She is my mother. I cannot go against her expressed commands" and—the temple to the foreign god will not be built.

But it is as foolish to talk to Wan-li as "to ask the loan of a comb from a Buddhist nun." She will not listen; or, if she does, a smile lies in the open lily of her face, and she bows her head in mock submission; then instantly lifts it again with new arguments learned from foreign books, and arguments that I in my ignorance cannot refute.

I feel that I am alone on a strange sea with this, my household; and I am in deadly fear that she will do some shocking thing, like those girls from the school in Foochow who, dressed in their brothers' clothing, came to Nanking and asked to be allowed to fight on the side of the republic. Patriotism is a virtue, but the battlefield is a man's place. Let the women stay at home and make the bandages to bind the wounded, and keep the braziers lighted to warm returning men.

I will not write you more of troubles, but I will tell you that your box of clothing came and is most welcome; also the cooking oil, which gave our food the taste of former days. The oils and sauces bought at shops are not so pure as those your servants make within the compound, nor does the cook here prepare things to my taste. Can you send me Feng-yi, who understands our customs? Your son has no great appetite, and I hope that food prepared in homely ways may tempt him to linger at the table longer. He is greatly overworked, and if he eats not well, with enjoyment of his rice, the summer will quite likely find him ill.

Your daughter and your family who touch your hand,
Kwei-li

My Dear Mother,

Your letter came, and I thank you for your advice. It is most difficult to act upon. I cannot shut Wan-li within an inner chamber, nor can I keep her without rice until she sees the wisdom of her ways. The times are truly different; we mothers of the present have lost our power to control our children, and cannot as in former days compel obedience. I can only talk to her; she laughs. I quote to her the words of the Sage: "Is any blessing better than to give a man a son, man's prime desire by which he and his name shall live beyond himself; a foot for him to stand on, a hand to stop his falling, so that in his son's youth he will be young again, and in his strength be strong." Be the mother of men; and I hear that that is China's trouble. She has too many children, too many thousands of clutching baby fingers, too many tiny mouths asking for their daily food. I am told, by this learned daughter of mine, that China has given no new thing to the world for many tens of centuries. She has no time to write, no time to think of new inventions; she must work for the morrow's rice. "How have you eaten?" is the salutation that one Chinese makes to another when meeting on a pathway; and in that question is the root of our greatest need. I am told that we are a nation of rank materialists; that we pray only for benefits that we may feel or see, instead of asking for the blessings of the Spirit to be sent us from above; that the women of my time and kind are the ruins of the country, with our cry of sons, sons!

But if our girls flaunt motherhood, if this thought of each one for himself prevails, what will become of us, a nation that depends upon its worship of the ancestors for its only practical religion? The loosening of the family bonds, the greater liberty of the single person, means the lessening of the restraining power of this old religion which depends upon the family life and the unity of that life. To do away with it is to do away with the greatest influence for good in China today. What will become of the filial piety that has been the backbone of our country? This family life has always been, from time immemorial, the foundation stone of our empire, and filial piety is the foundation stone of the family life that binds the Chinese people in bonds strong as ropes of twisted bamboo.

Our boys and girls will not listen; they are trying to be what they are not, trying to wear clothes not made for them, trying to be like nations and people utterly foreign to them; and they will not succeed. But, "into a sack holding a *ri* only a *ri* will go," and these sacks of our young people are full to overflowing with this, which seems to me dearly acquired knowledge, and there is not room for more. Time will help, and they will learn caution and discretion in life's halls of experience, and we can only guard their footsteps as best we may.

In the meantime, Mother of mine, my days are full and worried, and I, as in the olden time, can only come to you with my rice bowl filled with troubles and pour them all into your kindly lap. It is my only comfort, as your son is bitter and will not talk with patience, and it would not be seemly for me to open wide my heart to strangers; but I know you love me and are full of years and knowledge and will help me find the way.

Kwei-li

My Dear Mother,

These are most troubled times, and your son is harassed to the verge of sickness. Shanghai is filled with Chinese who come seeking foreign protection. Within the narrow confines of the foreign settlements, it is said, there are nearly a million Chinese, half of them refugees from their home provinces, fearing for their money or their lives, or both. The great red houses on the fashionable streets, built

by the English for their homes, are sold at fabulous prices to these
gentlemen, who have brought their families and their silver to the
only place they know where the foreign hand is strong enough to
protect them from their own people. There are many queer tales;
some are simply the breath of the unkind winds that seem to blow
from nowhere but gain in volume with each thing they touch. Tan
Toatai, who paid 300,000 *taels* for his position as *Taotai* of Shanghai,
and who left for his home province with 3,000,000 *taels*, as the gossips say, was asked to contribute from his plenty for the new government. He promised; then changed his mind, and carefully
gathered all his treasures together and left secretly one night for
Shanghai. Now he is in fear of his life and dares not leave the compound walls of the foreigner who has befriended him.

It makes one wonder what the use is of these fortunes that bring
endless sorrow by the misery of winning them, guarding them, and
the fear of losing them. They who work for them are as the water
buffalo who turns the waterwheel and gets but his daily food and
the straw-thatched hut in which he rests. For the sake of this food
and lodging, which falls to the lot of all, man wastes his true happiness—which is so hard to win.

These Chinese of the foreign settlements seem alien to me. Yuan
called upon your son the other day, and had the temerity to ask for
me—a most unheard-of thing. I watched him as he went away,
dressed in European clothes, as nearly all our younger men are
clothed these days, and one would never know that he had worn his
hair otherwise than short. There are no more neatly plaited braids
hanging down the back, and the beautiful silks and satins, furs and
peacock feathers are things of the past. These peacock feathers, em-
blems of our old officialdom, are now bought by foreign ladies as a
trimming on their hats. Shades of Li Hung-chang and Chang Chih-

tung! What will they say if looking over the barriers they see the insignia of their rank and office gracing the flowing headgear of the tourists who form great parties and come racing from over the seas to look at us as queer animals from another world?

It is not only the men who are copying the foreign customs and clothing. Our women are now seen in public, driving with their husbands, or walking arm in arm upon the public street. I even saw a Chinese woman driving that "devil machine," a motor car, with her own hands. She did not seem a woman, but an unsexed thing that had as little of womanhood as the car that took her along so swiftly. I promised to send Tah-li the new hair ornaments worn now. The old jewels are laid aside, the jade and pearls are things of the past. The hair is puffed and knotted in a way most unbecoming to the face. It is neither of the East nor of the West, but a half-caste thing, that brands its wearer as a woman of no race.

Do you remember the story over which the Chinese in all the empire laughed within their sleeves? Her Majesty, the Empress Dowager, was on most friendly terms with the wife of the Minister of the United States of America, and on one occasion gave her as a gift a set of combs enclosed within a box of silver. The foreign lady was delighted, and did not see the delicate sarcasm hidden within the present. Combs—the foreign ladies need them! We Chinese like the locks most smoothly brushed and made to glisten and shine with the scented elm, but they, the foreign ladies, allow them to straggle in rude disorder around their long, grave faces, which are so ugly in our eyes.

You asked me for the latest style in dress. It is impossible to say the latest style. Some women wear a jacket far too short and trousers tight as a coat sleeve. The modest ones still cover them with skirts; but I have seen women walking along the street who should

certainly stay within the inner courtyard and hide their shame. For
those who wear the skirt, the old, wide-pleated model has gone by,
and a long black skirt that is nearly European is now worn. It is not
graceful, but it is far better than the trousers worn by women who
walk along so stiffly upon their "golden lilies." These tiny feet to me
are beautiful, when covered with gay embroidery they peep from
scarlet skirts; but they too are passing, and we hear no more the
crying of the children in the courtyards. I am told that the small-
footed woman of China is one of the past, along with the long finger-
nails of our gentlemen and scholars; and I am asked why I do
not unbind my feet. I say, "I am too old; I have suffered in the
binding, why suffer in the unbinding?" I have conceded to the new
order by allowing unbound feet to all my girls, and everywhere my
family is held up as an example of the new Chinese. They do not
know of the many bitter tears I have shed over the thought that my
daughters would look like women of the servant class and perhaps
not make a good marriage; but I was forced to yield to their father,
whose foreign travel taught him to see beauty in the ugly, natural
feet. Even now when I see Wan-li striding across the grass, I blush
for her and wish she could walk more gracefully. My feet caused me
many moons of pain, but they are one of the great marks of my lady-
hood, and I yet feel proud as I come into a room with the gentle
swaying motions of the bamboo in a breeze; although my daughter
who supports me takes one great step to five of mine.

The curse of foot binding does not fall so heavily upon women
like myself, who may sit and embroider the whole day through, or,
if needs must travel, can be borne upon the shoulder of their chair
bearers, but it is a bane to the poor girl whose parents hope to have
one in the family who may marry above their station, and hoping
thus, bind her feet. If this marriage fails and she is forced to work

within her household, or, even worse, if she is forced to toil within the fields or add her mite gained by most heavy labor to help fill the many eager mouths at home, then she should have our pity. We have all seen the small-footed women pulling heavy boats along the towpath, or leaning on their hoes to rest their tired feet while working in the fields of cotton. To her each day is a day of pain; and this new law forbidding the binding of the feet of children will come as Heaven's blessing. But it will not cease at once, as so many loudly now proclaim. It will take at least three generations; her children's children will all quite likely have natural feet. The people far in the country, far from the noise and change and progress, will not feel immediately that they can wander so far afield from the old ideas of what is beautiful in their womanhood.

I notice, as I open wide my casement, that the rain has come, and across the distant fields it is falling upon the new-sown rice and seems to charm the earth into the thought that spring is here, bringing forth the faint green buds on magnolia, ash, and willow. Do you remember the verse we used to sing:

Oh she is good, the little rain, and well she knows our need,
Who cometh in the time of spring to aid the sun drawn seed.
She wanders with a friendly wind through silent heights unseen,
The furrows feel her happy tears, and lo, the land is green!

I must send a servant with the rain coverings for the children, that they may not get wet in returning from their schools.

We greet you, all.

Kwei-li

My Dear Mother,

Last night I heard a great wailing in the servants' courtyard, and found there the maid of your old friend Tang Tai-tai. She came from Nanking to us, as she has no one left in all the world. She is a Manchu and has lived all her life in the Manchu family of Tang within the Tartar city of Nanking. It seems the soldiers, besieging the city, placed their guns on Purple Hill, so that they would cause destruction only to the Tartar city, and it was leveled to the ground. No stone remains upon another; and the family she had served so faithfully were either killed in the battle that raged so fiercely, or were afterward taken to the grounds of Justice to pay with their lives for the fact that they belonged to the Imperial Clan. She is old, this faithful servant, and now claims my protection. It is another mouth to feed; but there is so much unhappiness that if it were within my power I would quench with rains of food and drink the anguish this cruel war has brought upon so many innocent ones. A mat on which to sleep, a few more bowls of rice, these are the only seeds that I may sow within the fields of love, and I dare not withhold them.

I am most sorrowful for these poor Manchus. For generations they have received a pension from the government; to every man-child an allowance has been made; and now they find themselves with nothing. Even their poor homes are piles of stone and rubbish. What will they do to gain their food in this great country, which is already full to overflowing? They are so pitiful, these old men and women thrown so suddenly upon the world. Their stories pierce my marrow, and I would that my sleeve were long and wide enough to cover all the earth and shelter these poor helpless ones. One old man—his years must have been nearly eighty—came to our door for help. I talked to him and found that until his sons were killed before his eyes, his home torn to the ground, he had never been outside the city's walls. He said, just like a child, "Why should I go? My wife, my sons, my home, my all, were within the walls; why go outside?"

Each hour brings us fresh rumors of the actions of the rebels. Poor Liang Tai-tai was here and in the sorest trouble. Her husband and her brother were officers in the army of Yuan, and when in Hanking were shot along with twenty of their brother officers, because they would not join the southern forces. To add to China's trouble, the southern pirates are attacking boats; and I am glad to say—although it sounds most cruel—that the government is taking measures both quick and just. Ten men were captured and were being brought by an English ship to Canton, and when in neutral waters it is said a Chinese gunboat steamed alongside with an order for the prisoners. As they stepped upon the Chinese boat, each man was shot. The English were most horrified, and have spoken loudly in all the papers of the acts of barbarism; but they do not understand our people. They must be frightened; especially at a time like this, when men are watching for the chance to take advantage of their country's turmoil.

These pirates of Canton have always been a menace. Each village in that country must forever be on the defensive, for no man is safe who has an ounce of gold. When Father was the prefect of Canton, I remember seeing a band of pirates brought to the *Yamen*, a ring of iron around the collarbone, from which a chain led to the prisoner on either side. It was brutal, but it allowed no chance of escape for these men, dead to all humanity, and desperate, knowing there awaited them long days of prison, and in the end they knew not what.

In those days imprisonment was the greatest of all evils; it was not made a place of comfort. For forty-eight long hours, the man within the clutches of the law went hungry; then, if no relative or friend came forth to feed him, he was allowed one bowl of rice and water for each day. A prison then meant ruin to a man with money, because the keepers of the inner gate, the guardian of the prison doors, the runners in the corridor, the jailer at the cell, each had a hand that arched for silver. A bowl of rice bought at the tea shop for ten *cash*, by the time the waiting hungry man received it, cost many silver dollars. Yet a prison should not be made a tempting place of refuge and vacation; if so, in times of cold and hunger it will be filled with those who would rather suffer shame than work.

Another thing the people who cry loudly against our old-time courts of justice do not understand is the crushing, grinding, naked poverty that causes the people in the overcrowded province to commit most brutal deeds. The penalties must match the deeds, and frighten other evil-doers. But—

What a subject for a letter! I can see you send for a cup of your fragrant sun-dried tea, mixed with the yellow flower of the jessamine, to take away the thoughts of death and evil and the wickedness of the world outside your walls. It will never touch you, Mother of mine, because the gods are holding you all safe within their loving hands.

Your daughter,
Kwei-li

9

My Mother,

I have most joyful news to tell you. My father has arrived! He came quite without warning, saying he must know the changing times from word of mouth instead of reading it in the papers. He has upset my household with his many servants. My father keeps to his old ways and customs and travels with an army of his people. His pipe man, his hat man, his cook, his boy—well, you remember when he descended upon us in Szechwan—yet he could bring ten times the number, and his welcome would be as warm. The whole town knows he is our guest, and foreigners and Chinese have vied with one another to do him honor. The foreign papers speak of him as "the greatest Chinese since Li Hung-chang," and many words are written about his fifty years' service as a high official. The story is retold of his loyalty to Her Majesty at the time of the Boxer Rebellion, when he threatened the foreigners that if Her Majesty was even frightened, he would turn his troops upon Shanghai and drive the foreigners into the sea. I wonder if the present government can gain the love the Dowager Empress drew from all who served her.

My father was the pioneer of the present education, so say the papers, and it is remembered that his school for girls in the province where he ruled nearly caused him the loss of his position, as His Excellency, Chang Chih-tung, said that women should not have book learning; that books would only give them a place in which to hide their threads and needles. It is also said of Father that he was against the coming of the foreigners. They could obtain no mine, no

railway, no concession in a province where he was representing his empress. China was closed, so far as lay within his power, even to men of religion from other lands. It was he who first said, "The missionary, the merchant, and then the gunboat."

My father will not talk about the present trials of China; he says, most justly, that he who is out of office should not meddle in the government. When asked if he will give the results of his long life and great experience to the republic, he answers that he owes his love and loyalty to the old regime under which he gained his wealth and honors; and then he shakes his head and says he is an old man, nothing but wet ashes. But they do not see the laughter in his eyes; for my father "is like the pine tree, ever green, the symbol of unflinching purpose and vigorous old age."

So many old-time friends have been to see him. Father, now that the heavy load of officialdom is laid aside, delights to sit within the courtyards with these friends and play at verse making. No man of his time is found lacking in that one great attribute of a Chinese gentleman. He has treasures of poetry that are from the pens of men who wrote of the longing for the spiritual life, or the beauties of the world outside their doors, or the pleasure of association with old and trusted friends. I read some scrolls the other day, and it was as though "aeolian harps had caught some strayed wind from an unknown world and brought its messages to me." It is only by the men of other days that poetry is appreciated, who take the time to look around them, to whom the quiet life, the life of thought and meditation is as vital as the air they breathe. To love the beautiful in life one must have time to sit apart from the worry and the rush of the present day. He must have time to look deep within his hidden self and weigh the things that count for happiness; and he must use most justly all his hours of leisure, a thing that modern life has taught us to hold lightly. . . .

My father learned to love the poets in younger days, but he still reads them over and over. He says they take him back to other years when life with all its dreams of beauty, love, and romance lay before him. It brings remembrance of youth's golden days when thoughts of fame and mad ambition came to him with each morning's light. This father of mine, who was stiffly bound with ceremony and acts of statecraft for ten long months of the year, had the temerity to ask two months' leave of absence from his duties, when he went to his country place in the hills, to his "Garden of the Pleasure of Peace." It was always in the early spring when "that goddess had spread upon the budding willow her lovely mesh of silken threads, and the rushes were renewing for the year." He sat beneath the bamboos swaying in the wind like dancing girls, and saw the jessamine and magnolia put forth their buds.

What happy days they were when father came! For me, who lived within the garden all the year, it was just a plain, great garden; but when he came it became a place of rare enchantment, with fairy palaces and lakes of jeweled water, and the lotus flowers took on a loveliness for which there is no name. We would sit hand in hand in our gaily painted teahouse, and watch the growing of the lotus from the first unfurling of the leaf to the fall of the dying flower. When it rained, we would see the leaves raise their eager, dark green cups until filled, then bend down gracefully to empty their fullness, and rise to catch the drops again.

The sound of the wind in the cane fields came to us at nighttime as we watched the shimmer of the fireflies. We sat so silently that the only thing to tell us that the wild duck sought his mate amidst the grass was the swaying of the reed stems, or the rising of the teal with whirring wings.

My father loved the silence, and taught me that it is in silence, in the quiet places, rather than on the housetops, that one can hear the spirit's call, and forget the clanging of the world. It is the great gift that the god of nature alone can give, and "he has found happiness who has won through the stillness of the spirit the Perfect Vision, and this stillness comes through contentment that is regardless of the world."

He often said to me that we are a caravan of beings, wandering through life's pathways, hungering to taste of happiness, which comes to us when we find plain food sweet, rough garments fine, and contentment in the home. It comes when we are happy in a simple way, allowing our wounds received in life's battles to be healed by the moonbeams, which send ointment more precious than the oil of sandalwood.

I could go on for pages, Mother of mine, of the lessons of my father, this grand old man, "who steeled his soul and tamed his thoughts and got his body in control by sitting in the silence and being one with nature, God, the maker of us all." And when I think of all these things, it is hard to believe that men who love the leisure, the poetry, the beautiful things of life, men like my father, must pass away. It seems to me it will be a day of great peril for China, for our young ones, when these men of the past lose their hold on the growing mind. As rapidly as this takes place, the reverence will be supplanted by discourtesy, faith by doubt, and love of the gods by unbelief and impiety.

Yet they say he does not stand for progress. What is progress? What is life? The poet truly cries: "How short a time it is that we are here! Why then not set our hearts at rest, why wear the soul with anxious thoughts? If we want not wealth, if we want not power, let us stroll the bright hours as they pass, in gardens amidst the flowers, mounting the hills to sing our songs, or weaving verses by the lily ponds. Thus may we work out our allotted span, content with life, our spirits free from care."

My father has a scroll within his room that says:

For fifty years I plodded through the vale of lust and strife,
Then through my dreams there flashed a ray of the old sweet
    peaceful life.
No scarlet-tasseled hat of state can vie with soft repose;
Grand mansions do not taste the joys that the poor man's cabin
    knows.
I hate the threatening clash of arms when fierce retainers throng,
I loathe the drunkard's revels and the sound of fife and song;
But I love to seek a quiet nook, and some old volume bring
Where I can see the wildflowers bloom and hear the birds in
    spring.

Ah, dear one, my heart flows through my pen, which is the messenger of the distant soul to you, my Mother.

Kwei-li

10

My Dear Mother,

My days are passed like a waterwheel awhirl, and I can scarcely find time to attend to the ordinary duties of my household. I fear I seem neglectful to you, and I will try to be more regular with my letters, so that you will not need to reproach me. Tonight my house is quiet and all are sleeping, and I can chat with you without the many interruptions that come from children, servants, and friends during the waking hours.

I have had callers all the day; my last, the wife of the Japanese Consul, who brought with her her two children. They were like little butterflies, dressed in their kimonos and bright red *obis*, their straight black hair framing their tiny elfin faces. I was delighted and could scarcely let them go. Their mother says she will send me their photographs, and I will send them to you, as they seem children from another world. They are much prettier, in my eyes, than the foreign children, with their white hair and colorless blue eyes, who always seem to be clothed in white. That seems unnatural for a child, as it is our mourning color, and children should wear gay colors, as they are symbols of joy and gladness.

My husband watched them go away with looks of hatred and disdain within his eyes, and when I called them Butterflies of Gay Nippon, he gave an ejaculation of great disgust, as at this time he is not fond of the Japanese. He believes, along with others, that they are helping the rebels with their money, and we know that many Japanese officers are fighting on the side of the southern forces. He

could not forget the words I used, "Dainty Butterflies," and he said
that these dainty butterflies are coming far too fast, at the rate of
many tens of thousands each year; they must be fed and clothed and
lodged, and Japan is far too small. These pretty babies searching for
a future home are China's greatest menace. Japan feels that her destiny lies here in the Far East, where she is overlord, and will con-
tinue as such until the time, if it ever comes, when new China, with
her far greater wealth and her myriads of people, disputes the
power of the little island. At present there is no limit to Japan's ambition. Poor China! It will take years and tens of years to mold her
people into a nation; and Japan comes to her each year, buying her
rice, her cotton, and her silk.

These wily merchants travel up her pathways and traverse her
rivers and canals, selling, buying, and spreading their influence
abroad. There are eight thousand men of Japan in Shanghai, keen
young men, all looking for the advantage of their country. There is
no town of any size where you cannot find a Japanese. They have
driven the traders of other nationalities from many places; the
Americans especially have been compelled to leave; and now there is
a bitter struggle between the people of the British Isles and the Japanese for the trade of our country. In the olden time the people
from Great Britain controlled the trade of our Yang-tse Valley, but
now it is almost wholly Japanese.

The British merchant, in this great battle, has the disadvantage
of being honest, while the trader from Japan has small thought of
honesty to hold him to a business transaction. We say here, "One
can hold a Japanese to a bargain as easily as one can hold a slippery catfish on a gourd." The Sons of Nippon have another point in
their favor: The British merchant is a Westerner, while the Japanese uses to the full his advantage of being an Oriental like our-

selves. Trade—trade—is what Japan craves, and it is according to
its need that she does; her diplomacy, her suavity is based upon it;
her army and her vast navy are to help gain and hold it; it is the
end and aim of her ambitions.

We Chinese have people—millions, tens of millions of them.
When they are better educated, when China is more prosperous,
when new demands and higher standards of living are created, when
the coolie will not be satisfied with his bowl of rice a day and his
one blue garment, then possibilities of commerce will be unlimited.
Japan sees this with eyes that look far into the future, and she
wants to control this coming trade—and I fear she will. She has an
ambition that is as great as her overpowering belief in herself, an
ambition to be in the East what England is in the West; and she is
working patiently, quietly, to that end. We fear her; but we are
helpless. I hear the men talk bitterly; but what can they do? We
must not be another Korea; we must wait until we are strong, and
look to other hands to help us in our struggle.

We hope much from America, that country which has so wonderful an influence upon us, which appeals to our imagination because it is great and strong and prosperous. The suave and
humorous American, with his easy ways, is most popular with our
people, although he cannot always be trusted nor is his word bond.
He is different from the man of England, who is not fond of people
not of his own color and will not try to disguise the fact. He is cold
and shows no sympathy to those of an alien race, although we must
admit he always acts with a certain amount of justice. America is
contemptuous of China and her people, but it is a kindly contempt,
not tinged with the bitterness of the other powers, and we hope, because of trade interest (the American is noted for finding and holding the place that yields him dollars), she will play the part of a

kindly friend and save China from her enemies who are now watching each other with such jealous eyes. There is another reason why we like America: She does not seem to covet our land. I would that she and England might form a bond of brotherhood for our protection; because all the world knows that where Germany, Russia, or Japan has power, all the people from other lands are barred by close-shut doors.

Since hearing my husband talk I see those babies with other eyes, with eyes of knowledge and dislike. I see them becoming one of the two great classes in Japan—merchants with grasping hand to hold fast all they touch, or men of war. There is no other class. . . .

We have a proverb, "Even a monkey falls"; and some distant day the Western world that thinks so highly of Japan will see beneath the surface and will leave her; the great pagoda she has built without foundation will come tumbling down like the houses of sand my children build in the garden. It will be seen that they are like their beautiful kimonos, which hang so gracefully in silken folds. But take away the kimonos, and the sons and daughters of that empire are revealed in all their ugliness—coarse, heavy, sensual, with no grace or spirit life to distinguish them from animals.

Do I speak strongly, my Mother? We feel most strongly the action of the Japanese in this, our time of trouble. We have lost friends; the husbands, brothers, fathers of our womenfolk are lying in long trenches because of training given to our rebels by members of that race. I should not speak so frankly, but it is only to you that I can say what is within my heart. I must put the bar of silence across my lips with all save you; sitting here within the courtyard I hear all that goes on in *Yamen*, shop, and women's quarters. One need not leave one's doorway to learn of the great world. I hear my sons speak of new China, and many things I do not understand; my husband and his friends talk more sedately, for they are watching, thoughtful men, trying hard to steer this, our ship of state, among the rocks that now beset it close on every side. My daughters bring their friends, my servants their companions, and the gossip of our world is emptied at my feet.

The clock strikes one, and all the world's asleep except

Kwei-li

11

Dear Mother,

She is here, my daughter-in-law, and I can realize in a small degree your feelings when I came to your household. I know you were prepared to give me the same love and care that my heart longs to give this, the wife of my eldest son. I also know how she feels in this strange place, with no loved faces near her, with the thought that perhaps the new home will mean the closed door of a prison, and the husband she never saw until the marriage day the jealous guardian thereof. I have tried to give her welcome and let her see that she is heart of our hearts, a part of us.

She is different from the young girls I have seen these latter days, different from my daughters, and — I may say it to you, my Mother — a sweeter, dearer maiden in many ways. She has been trained within the courtyard in the old-fashioned customs that make for simplicity of heart, grace of manner, which give obedience and respect to older people; and she has the delicate, high-bred ways that our girls seem to feel unnecessary in the hurry of these days. She takes me back to years gone by, where everything is like a dream, and I can feel again the chair beneath me that carried me up the mountainside with its shadowing of high woods, and hear the song of water falling gently from far-off mountain brooks, and the plaintive cry of flutes unseen, which came to welcome me to my new home.

With her dainty gowns, her tiny shoes, her smooth black hair, she is a breath from another world, and my sons and daughters regard her as if she were a stray butterfly, blown hither by some wind too strong for her slight wings. She is as graceful as the slender willow, her youthful charm is like the cherry tree in bloom, and the sweet thoughts natural to youth and the springtime of life flow from her heart as pure as the snow-white blossoms of the plum tree. She does not belong to this, our modern world; she should be bending with iris grace above goldfish in the ponds, or straying in gardens where there are lakes of shimmering water murmuring beneath great lotus flowers that would speak to her of love.

We are all more than charmed, and gather to the sunshine she has brought. As they knelt before us for our blessing, I thought what a happy thing is youth and love. "Kings in their palaces grow old, but youth dwells forever at contentment's side."

But I must tell you of the marriage. Instead of the red chair of marriage, my new daughter-in-law was brought from the house of her uncle in that most modern thing, a motor car. I insisted that it be covered with red satin, the color of rejoicing; and great rosettes trailed from the corners to the ground. The feasting was elaborate and caused me much care in its preparation, as not only had been

provided the many different kinds of food for our Chinese friends, but foreigners, who also came, were served dishes made expressly for them, and with foreign wines, of which they partook most liberally. The Europeans, men and women, ate and drank together with a freedom that to me is most unseemly, and I cannot understand the men who have no pride in their women's modesty but allow them to sit at table with strange men close by their side. Behind the archway, we Chinese women "of the old school," as my daughter calls us, feasted and laughed our fill, just as happy as if parading our new gowns before the eyes of stranger-men.

Li-ti is delighted with your gift, the chain of pearls. It is a most appropriate present, for "pearls belong of right to her whose soul reflects the color of youth's purity"; and I, I am so happy in this new life that has come to dwell beneath our rooftree. I had many fears that she would not be to my liking, that she would be a modern Chinese woman; and another one, oh, Mother of mine, would fill to overflowing my bowl of small vexations; but the place is perfumed by her scent, the scent of sandalwood, which represents the China that I love, and flowers of jessamine and purple hyacinths and lilies-of-the-valley, which speak to us of youth and spring and love and hope.

Your daughter, who gives the messages from all your family, who touch your hand with deep respect.

12

My Dear Mother,

I am sorry that you have been troubled by news of fighting within the province. All is well with us, as we sent you word by telegraph. If anything happens that touches any of your household, we will send you word at once.

This town is a hotbed of rebellion, and it is all because the rebels have been enabled to perfect their plans through the existence of the foreign settlements. How I dislike these foreigner adventurers! I wish they would take their gilded dust, their yellow gold, and leave us to our peace; but they walk our streets as lord and masters, and allow the plotting traitors to make their plans, and we are helpless. If I were China's ruler and for one day had power, there would not be one white man left within the borders of my country. We hear each day of friends who give their lives on the field of battle — these battles and this conflict that would not exist were it not for the foreign powers, who within these settlements, protect the low-browed ruffians who are plotting China's ruin. . . .

These foreigners rate China low, who have never met a Chinese gentleman, never read a line of Chinese literature, and who look at you with ignorance if you mention the names of our sages. They see no Chinese except their servants, and they judge the world about them from that low point of view. I know a lady here who is a leader in their society, a woman who has lived within our land for many tens of years; when asked to meet a prince of our house imperial, she declined, saying she never associated with Chinese.

A prince to her was no more than any other yellow man; she said she would as soon think of meeting her gate coolie at a social tea. How can there be a common meeting ground between our people and the average European, of whom this woman is a representative and who is not alone in her estimation of the people amongst whom she lives but whom she never sees? They get their knowledge of China from servants, from missionaries who work among the lower classes, and from the newspaper reports that are always to the disadvantage of our people. . . .

Poor China! She is first clubbed on the head and then stroked on the back by these foreigners, her dear friends. Friends! It is only when the cold season comes that we know the pine tree and the cypress to be evergreens, and friends are known in adversity. The foreigners who profess to be our friends are waiting and hoping for adversity to come upon us, that they may profit by it. They want our untouched wealth, our mines of coal and iron and gold, and it is upon them they have cast their eyes of greed. . . .

Your son has been trying to settle a foreign case. Some men from America went to Ningpo, and talked long and loud of the darkness of the city, its streets dangerous in the nighttime, its continual fires caused by the flickering lamps of oil that are so constantly overturned by the many children. They told the officials that the times were changing, that to walk the streets with a lighted lantern in the hand is to lose step with the march of progress. They showed the benefits of the large lights of electricity blazing like a sun on each corner of the great city, making it impossible for robbers and evildoers to carry on their work in darkness. They promised to turn nighttime into day, to put white lights in *Yamen*, office, and household. There should be a light beneath each rooftree, at no greater expense than the bean-oil lamp. They were most plausible, and many thousands of silver dollars were brought forth and given to the men as contract money. They left us to buy machinery; the years have passed; they never have returned. Ningpo still has streets of darkness, men still walk abroad with lighted lanterns, the bean-oil lamp is seen within the cottage and—will be until the hills shall fade, so far as the officials are concerned, who once dreamed dreams of a city lit by the light as of myriad suns.

"When a man has been burned once with hot soup he forever after blows upon cold rice"; so these men of China will think long before trusting again a foreigner with their silver.

How can the missionaries have the face to come here with their religion, when the dissolute white man is in every port manifesting lust and greed and brutality, which Chinese are accustomed to associate with the citizenship and religion attributed to Christianity. No wonder it is hard for them to make converts among the people who have business dealings with these men from Christian nations.

But China will not forever bear the ill-treatment of men from Western lands. She is awake to all the insults; she has learned in the bitter halls of experience. She sleeps no longer; she will rise in self-defense and fight aggression; and the nations who have misused her must remember that when she moves it will be the movement of a mighty people aroused by the thought of their great wrongs. She is peaceful and long-suffering, but she is different from the old-time China. She has now a national spirit that has been brought about by better means of communication between provinces. In the olden time it was difficult for one part of the empire to know the conditions in another. But now the telegraph and the daily newspaper come to all the smallest villages. I am sure that the watchman by your outer gate reads as he guards your household, and learns in far Szechwan what has happened today in Peking, or the southern city of Canton, and the news is discussed in the tea shops and on corners by men from farm and shop and office.

The foreigners are mistaken in their belief that China can ever be united. She has been one for centuries, in beliefs, in morals, in education, and in religion, and now she will be more united in her stand against the hated white man who covets her treasures. She may quarrel with her brothers within her borders; but that is nothing but a family feud, and in time of danger from outside, like all families, she will unite to fight for her own until the last red lantern fades and the morning star is shining.

Enough of politics and bitterness! I hear your son, who is coming for his evening cup of tea.

Your daughter,
Kwei-li

My Dear Mother,

The times here are very bad; people are fleeing from the inland cities and coming to Shanghai by the thousands. The place is crowded to suffocation.

Wu Ting-fang was here and talked long into the night with my husband. My son, who, I am afraid, does not think too highly of this great man, says that he is with the party that is "on top," that he spends most of his time sitting on the fence—whatever that may mean. I drove past his house the other day and did not see him sitting on the fence, but on his veranda, calmly drinking tea.

Sun Yat-sen has violated his word of honor and has joined the southern forces. We feel he has acted most dishonorably and (my son again) should have "stayed bought." Gossips say he received many millions of *taels*, presumably for the railroads, but that was only an excuse to slip the money into his wide and hungry pockets.

It is decided to send my son to Canton, into the office of the governor of that province. We are glad to get him away from Shanghai, which is a nest of adders and vipers, conspiring and raising their poisonous heads in the dark. One does not know whom to trust, or who may prove to be a traitor.

Li-ti, his wife, wishes to go with him, and weeps the whole day through because we will not permit it. She is not well, and we tell her she will not really be separated from her husband, because, as the poets tell us, people who love, though at a distance from each other, are like two lutes tuned in harmony and placed in adjoining rooms. When you strike the *kung* note on one, the *kung* note on the other will answer, and when you strike the *cho* note on the one the *cho* other will give the same sound. They are both tuned to the same pitch, when the influence of the keynote, love, is present.

I took my son aside the other night and said, "I am your mother and I want to speak words to you straight from the heart. You are to have the joy of work, and remember the pride of work lies in the thought 'For me alone is the task.' " I tried to make him understand that praise, glory, and honors are good, but they do not make for long life, and especially in these times it is better to work quietly without attracting too much attention. It is more safe, for "he who raises himself on tiptoe cannot stand, and he who stretches his legs wide apart cannot walk."

His father was especially anxious that he not be pierced with the arrow of treachery that poisons the blood and finds the weak spot in the armor of so many of our young men. He told him to keep himself above suspicion, to avoid those entangled in the nets of double dealing of whom one is uncertain, because "the red glow of the morning sun seems to stain even the pure whiteness of the new-fallen snow."

Why, Mother of mine, did you send the old priest from the temple down here? He abides in the courtyard, squatting on his heels, serving the spirits neither of Heaven nor of earth, but he sits and talks and talks with the women of the courtyards. There are some of them I would send to a far-off province, especially Fang Tai, the mother of our gateman.

"A woman with a long tongue is a flight of steps leading to calamity."

This priest of yours has been quarreling with her now over the question of the son of Wong Tai, who is accused of being on too friendly terms with some of the leaders of the rebellion. He made the unfortunate remark that perhaps the man was innocent but "one does not arrange his headdress under an apricot tree, nor his foot gear in a melon patch, if he wishes to be above suspicion," and this simple remark has called down upon his priestly head the wrath of all the women. I think he will go to the monastery within the city to pass the night—at least if he has wisdom equal to his years.

Yesterday I thought that I might make some use of him, and I felt when he was working he would not be stirring up the courtyards. I bade him write the Sage's words upon a scroll of satin for my boy to take with him to his new home. He did it very beautifully, as he is a real artist with the brush. This is the reading of the scroll:

There are three things for a man to guard against:
The lusts of the flesh in early years,
The spirit of combativeness in middle-age,
And ambition as the years go on.
There are three things to command your reverence:
The ordinances of Heaven,
Great men, and the words of the sages.
There are three times three things to be remembered:
To be clear in vision,
Quick in hearing,
Kindly in expression,

Respectful in demeanor,
True in word,
Serious in duty,
Inquiring in doubt,
Self-controlled in anger,
And just and fair when the chair of success is before your door.

I made a roll of it and placed it upon his desk, and when he opened it he found within another scroll of silk, the same in color, size, and finish, written by his most unfilial sisters, which read:

Remember that thou art young.
What thou *dost* know is not to be compared
With what thou dost *not* know.

It made him angry at first, but I do not know but that the shorter scroll contains the greater wisdom.

I am anxious for this boy of mine, who is starting to sail his ship of manhood across the Broad River of Life in these most perilous times. I think he is strong enough to conquer all, but I have lighted candles and bought fine incense to persuade the gods to temper winds to untried hands.

> Your daughter,
> Kwei-li

14

My Dear Mother,

I have not written you for several days. We are in Nanking, where my husband is presiding at a meeting of the officials in order to discuss the question of a compromise, or to try in some way to settle the questions that are causing this dreadful rebellion, without more loss of life. He is also acting as judge in the case of some of the men who have been caught pillaging and destroying the homes of innocent people. It is hard for him to act with strict justice, remembering the many friends he has lost, and it is necessary to see things without their individuality in order to be wise in all judgments. I came, ostensibly to see the friends of my childhood, but really to take care of your son and see that he eats with regularity and takes his rest. He is working far too hard. He gives himself to whatever task arrives, greedy for the work, like one who lusts in the delight of seeing tasks accomplished. But he is trusted by all, both sides agreeing to rest on his decisions, all realizing that personal feeling is put far into the background of his mind when the interests of new China are at stake.

We are in the *Yamen* where I lived as a young girl, but now all is changed. Instead of the guard of honor, with their great flapping hats, their gaily decorated jackets, baggy trousers tucked into velvet boots, pennants flying from their spear points as their small ponies dashed madly in front of the official carriage, we were met by a body of foreign-dressed soldiers who conducted us with military precision quite different from the old-time dash and lack of discipline.

Inside the *Yamen*, things are also different. Everything is orderly and moves with a machinelike regularity that seems totally foreign to an Eastern official's residence. There is not the democracy of other days; the man from the street, the merchant or the coolie with his burden on his shoulders, did not follow us into the courtyards to see what was being done, nor were there crowds of idle men gazing with mild curiosity at the visitors to their city.

We hear much of the old-time power of the officials; but things are not nearly as democratic under this new government as in former times, when, it is true, the governor had the power of life and death, but still was obliged to deal leniently with his people. A little larger demand for tribute, a case of rank injustice, and he became the object of the people's wrath and would quite likely see his *Yamen* in a blaze, or pay with his life for his greed. The masses held real power within their hands. If their officials did not deal justly with them, they caused a riot, and if the frightened official could not still it within a certain time, he was told that he evidently could not control his people and so was removed.

My husband inspected the regiments stationed here. I saw them from a veranda in the *Yamen* where we women were unseen. Fifteen thousand men marched past him; they were a sight for one who loves his country. They were all young men, none seeming over twenty-five, and as they marched my heart was filled with pride and hope in them. I thought, it is of just such men, such sons of peasants and working people, that Japan made her army that gained a victory over one of the greatest nations in the Western world. Why cannot we, with our unlimited numbers, make an army that will cause our country to be respected and take its place among the powers of the world? We have the men, myriads and myriads of them; men who are used to hardship and privation in their daily life, who, on a bowl of rice, a morsel of dried fish, can fight the whole day through. Our men are not accustomed to the luxuries of the foreigners, who, even in times of war, carry great stores of what seems to Eastern nations unnecessary baggage. With them their endless string of wagons is their greatest pitfall, and with us these latter could be reduced to the smallest count.

Yet we hear on every hand that the courage of the Chinese soldier is held at low value. But why? When sent unarmed, or with guns for which there were no bullets, into the Japanese war, against troops with the latest inventions in weapons to kill, the only thing to be done was to retreat. But when they are paid, fed, and armed, and have leaders who will go to the front with them, instead of saying "There is the enemy. Charge! I will go back to the hills and await your hour of glory," they are found to be courageous to the verge of fanaticism. Under trusted leaders there is no forlorn hope or desperate service for which they would not volunteer. Let them have confidence in their new generals, and, even though not understanding the cause, they will make the best soldiers in the world.

But I must not talk to you of war; we do not want more bloodshed and the fatherless homes and lean years that follow in the track

of great armies. Yet, if we cannot be without it, let it serve war's
ends—the ultimate safety of our people, and bring them peace and
tranquillity, their heart's desire.

I visited the ruined homes of friends of mine, who are no more.
It made me feel life is nothing but a mirage, a phantom, or as foam,
and "even as all earthly vessels made on the potter's wheel must end
by being broken, so end the lives of men." I went out to the home
of Yuan Tai-tai, who, to my childish mind was the great lady of my
dreams. I can close my eyes and see her still, like a brilliant butterfly, dressed in her gay brocades, her hair twined with jewels of pearl
and jade; with hand in mine she wandered over her garden, bending
over goldfish ponds, or clipping fading flowers from off their stems.
There reigned a heavy silence in her palace, with its memories, full
of sadness and a vague regret, reminding me of an old blue China
bowl, which a hand of other days had filled with roses. The flowers
trying to struggle from beneath the thorns and brambles that always
come where troops are quartered, seemed to say, "Behold, they are
not here who once have cared for us and cherished us, but the
gardens breathe of them and we are fragrant for their sakes." I
picked a branch of cherry blossoms, and swiftly the perfumed pet-
als fell to the ground—symbols of the dainty lives that bloomed so
short a time in this fair garden of my lady. Liu Che, the poet of
the olden time, seems to have been speaking to this, my friend,
when he says:

> The sound of rustling silk is stilled,
> With dust the marble courtyard filled;
> No footfalls echo on the floor,
> Fallen leaves in heaps block up the door . . .
> For she, my pride, my lovely one is lost.

We went from Yuan's palace to the Temple of Kwan-yin, which I often visited as a child. It also was a ruin, but it spoke to me of the dead thousands of weary feet that had climbed the steps leading to its shrines; of the buried mothers who touched the floor before its altars with reverent heads and asked blessings on their children's lives; of their children, taught to murmur prayers to the Mother of all Mercies, who held close within her loving heart the sorrows, hopes, and fears of woman's world. Ghosts of these spirits seemed to follow as we wandered through deserted courtyards, and an odor as of old incense perfumed the air. I went out and stood upon the tortoise that is left to guard the ruined temple; the great stone tortoise that is the symbol of longevity of our country, that even armies in their wrath cannot destroy.

From the gateway we could

see the river, a gleaming thread of silver, and the hillsides, tree clad, flower wreathed, painted with the colors that the gods give to the spring—the spring that "thrills the warm blood into wine." But I miss the natural songs that should float upward from the valley, and down the reed-strewn banks of the canals, where laborers in olden days were happy in their toil.

Even as we left, the pattering raindrops came as rice grains falling upon the threshing floor, and the hills seemed "folding veils of sorrow round their brows." It was brought to our remembrance that we must return to a city where war and famine may come thundering at her gates, and we must stand with helpless hands.

Dear Mother mine, stay upon your flower-scented balustrade, and drink great draughts of that wine of spring, the vintage of the wise, which the gods give to you freely in your mountain home, and leave to younger hands the battles with the world. You must not come; write no more that you would be amongst us. We love you dearly, but we would cherish you and keep you from all care.

Kwei-li

15

My Dear Mother,

I have had a most interesting day, and I hasten to tell you all about it. I have just returned from opening a home for motherless children, given by a mission of a foreign land. It is a beautiful thought, and a kindly one, to give a home to these poor waifs of an alien land, all in the name of their Savior of the World. I saw for the first time a picture of this Christ, with little children around Him. The message I read within His eyes seemed to be: "I will be father and mother and playmate to all little children."

I looked at the picture and at the people around me on the platform, and wondered why in all the Christian world that claims this loving Master there should be such exceeding bitterness among His followers. How can they expect us to believe in this great Teacher when they themselves are doubtful of his message, and criticize quite openly their Holy Book? If it is true, should education and science make its teaching less authentic? We do not want a religion that is uncertain to its own people, yet we take with many thanks what it can give us, the things we understand, such as their schools and hospitals. Where there is pain or ignorance, there is no distinction in the god that brings relief. We may not believe in the doctrines that we are taught in the waiting rooms of their hospitals, but we do believe in the healing power of the medicines that are brought by religious zeal from over the seas.

If their teaching has not as yet made many converts, the effect has been great in the spread of higher ideals of education. And much of the credit for the progress of our modern life must be given to the mission schools, which, directly or indirectly, have opened new pathways in the field of education for our country, and caused the youth of China to demand a higher learning throughout the land. This aggressive religion from the West, coupled with the education that seems to go hand in hand with it, is bound to raise the religious plane of China by forcing our dying faiths to reassume higher and higher forms in order to survive.

But I believe that these teachers from the foreign lands should understand better the religions they are so anxious to displace, and instead of always looking for the point of difference or weakness in our faith, should search more anxiously for the common ground, the spark of the true light that may still be blown to flame, finding the altar that may be dedicated afresh to the true God.

Every religion, however imperfect, has something that ought to be held sacred, for there is in all religions a secret yearning after the unknown God. This thought of God "is an elixir made to destroy death in the world, and unfailing treasure to relieve the poverty of mankind, a balm to allay his sickness, a tree under which may rest all creatures wearied with wanderings over life's pathways. It is a bridge for passing over hard ways, open to all wayfarers, a moon of thought arising to cool the fever of the world's sin, and whatever name His followers may call Him, he is the one True God of all mankind."

Whether we see the coolie bowing his head before the image of the Lord of Light, the Buddha, or the peasant woman with her paper money alight in the brazier at the feet of Kwan-yin, we ought to feel that the place where he who worships stands is holy ground. We hear it said that he is worshiping an image, an idol, a thing of stone or wood or clay. It is not so; he is thinking far beyond the statue, he is seeing God. He looks upward toward the sky and asks what supports that cup of blue. He hears the winds and asks them whence they come and where they go. He rises for his toil at break of day and sees the morning sun start on his golden journey. And Him who is the cause of all these wonders, he calls his Life, his Breath, his Lord of All. He does not believe that the idol is his God. " 'Tis to the light which Thy splendor lends to the idol's face, that the worshiper bends." . . .

We of the East "have sounded depth on depth only to find still deeper depths unfathomed and profound," and we have learned to say that no sect or religion can claim to be in possession of *all* the Truth. Let the teachers from other countries learn of our doctrines. Let them learn of Buddha. To one who reads his pure teaching, nothing so beautiful, nothing so high, has been heard in all the world. We admit that, little by little, changes have come, simplicity has been lost, and with every addition something departed from its purity and it became stained. Yet I believe that much of the kindliness, much of the gentleness now so marked in Chinese nature, may be traced to the teaching of this great apostle of peace and quietude. . . .

All have a hunger of the soul for something besides life's meat and drink; all want a remedy for the sorrows of the world. The Buddhists believe that it can be found in the destruction of desire, by renouncing the world and following the noble path of peace until death shall open the portals of the unknowable, everlasting stillness from which there is no return. The Confucianists say the remedy is found within the world by fulfilling all its duties and leaving to a greater Justice the future and its rewards. The Christians give a whispered message of hope to the lonely soul beating against the bars of the world about him, and say that a life of love and joy and peace is the gift of their great Messenger, and when the years have passed that He stands within an archway to welcome those, His chosen, to a land of bliss where we shall meet all who have loved us and whom we have loved in life, and gaze upon His face.

Which is *the* Way, which path to God is broad enough for all the world?

Kwei-li

My Dear Mother,

I received your letter, which was full of reproaches most unjust. I have not broken my word, given to you so long ago. I opened the home for friendless children, not because it belonged to a mission of a foreign religion, but because I think it a most worthy cause.

There are many homeless little ones in this great city, and these people give them food and clothing and loving care, and because it is given in the name of God not found within our temples, is that a reason for withholding our encouragement?

You have made my heart most heavy. Twenty-five years ago, when my first son was taken from me, I turned from gods who gave no comfort in my time of need: all alone with hungry winds of bitterness gnawing the lute strings of my desolate mother-heart, I stood upon my terrace and fought despair. My days were without hope

16

·

·

·

145

and my nights were long hours filled with sorrow, when sleep went trailing softly by and left me to the old dull pain of memory. I called in anguish upon Kwan-yin, and she did not hear my prayer. The painted smile upon her lips but mocked me, and in despair I said, "There are no gods," and in my lonely court of silent dreams I lost the thread of worldly care until my tiny bark of life was nearly drifting out upon the unknown sea.

You remember that the servants brought me from out the marketplace the book of the foreign god, and in its pages I woke to life again. I looked once more from out my curtained window, and saw the rosy glow of dawn instead of gray, wan twilights of the hopeless days before me; and, as on a bridge half-seen in shadows dim, I returned to the living world about me. You said nothing until it had brought its healing, then you took the book and kept it from me. You told me with tears that it would bring your head in sorrow to your resting place upon the hillside if I left the gods of my ancestors and took unto my heart the words and teachings of the gods of an alien race. I promised you that I would not cause you grief, and I have kept my word.

In my ignorance I have longed for knowledge, for someone to explain the teaching that rolled away for me the rush of troubled waters that flooded all my soul; but as I looked about me and saw the many warring factions that follow the great Teacher of love and peace, I did not know which way to turn, which had the truth to give me; and I wanted *all*, not part. I have this book, and have not sought wisdom from outside, but only search its pages to find its messages to me.

You must not say I have deserted China's gods, nor is it just to write that my children are wandering from the Way. I have observed the feasts and fastings; each morn the Household God has

rice and tea before him; the Kitchen God has gone with celebrations
at springtime to the spirit up above. The candles have been lighted
and the smoke of incense has ascended to propitiate the God of
Light, Lord Buddha, and Kwan-yin, and my children have been
taught their prayers and holy precepts. It is not my fault, nor should
you blame it on my teaching, if rites and symbols have lost their
meaning, and if the gods of China are no longer strong enough to
hold our young.

Oh, Mother of mine, you know I would not cause you sorrow,
and you have hurt me sorely with your letter of bitterness and reproach. If you could have seen within my heart these many years,
and known the longing for this light that came to me in darkness,
then you would not have burned the book that brought me hope
and life again when all seemed gone.

You asked me to promise you anew that I will not trouble your
last few years with thoughts that seem to you a sacrilege and a dese-
cration of your gods. You are the mother of my husband, and it is
to you that I owe all loyalty and obedience. I promise you, but—
that which is deep within my heart—is *mine*.

Your daughter,
Kwei-li

My Dear Mother,

I, your son's wife, have been guilty of the sin of anger, one of the seven deadly sins—and great indeed has been my anger. Ting-fang has been bringing home with him lately the son of Wong Kai-kia, a young man who has been educated abroad, I think in Germany. I have never liked him, have looked upon his aping of the foreign manners, his half-long hair which looks as if he had started a queue [braid] again and then stopped, his stream of words without beginning and without end, as a foolish boy's small vanities that would pass as the years and wisdom came. But now—how can I tell you—he asks to have my daughter as his wife, my Luh-meh, my flower. If he had asked for Man-li, who wishes to become a doctor, I might have restrained my anger; but, no, he wants the beauty of our household, and for full a space of ten breaths' breathing time, I withheld my indignation, for I was speechless. Then I fear I talked, and only stopped for lack of words. My son is most indignant, and says I have insulted his dear friend. His dear friend, indeed! He is so veiled in self-conceit that he can be insulted by no one; and as for being a friend, he does not know the word unless he sees in it something to further his own particular interests.

I told my son that he is a man who leads a life of idleness and worse. The teahouse knows him better than his rooftree. He is most learned and has passed safely many examinations, and writes letters at the end of his name, and has made a special study of the philosophers of the present time; and because of this vast amount of book

learning and his supposedly great intelligence he is entitled to in-
dulgence, says my son, and should not be judged by the standards
that rule ordinary people, who live upon a lower plane. I say that
his knowledge and greater intelligence (which latter I very much
doubt) increase his responsibilities and should make of him an example for the better living of men.

A clever bad man is like vile characters scrawled in ink of gold,
and should be thrown aside as fit only for the braziers.

He is handsome in my daughter's eyes; but I say virtue is within
the man, not upon his skin. He fascinates my younger sons with his
philosophy and his teahouse oratory. I do not like philosophy, it is
marked with the stamp of infidelity and irreligion. It is rarely that a
man devotes himself to it without robbing himself of his faith, and
casting off the restraints of his religion; or, if they do not lose it
utterly, they so adulterate it with their philosophic writings, so full
of vain and delusive reasonings, that it is impossible to separate the
false from the true. The reading of philosophic writings should be
forbidden to our young folk, just as the slippery banks of a river are
forbidden to one who knows not how to swim. I will have none of
them in our library, nor will I allow their father to read them where
his sons can see him. The snake charmer should not touch the ser-
pents before his child's eyes, knowing that the child will try to imitate him in all things.

It is "as pouring water in a frog's face" to talk to these, my children, who think a man, with words upon his lips, a sage. I say a
dog is not a good dog because he is a good barker, nor should a
man be considered a good man because he is a good talker; but I
see only pity in their faces that their mother is so far behind the
times. These boys of ours are so attracted by the glimpses they have
had of European civilization, that they look down upon their own

nationality. They have been abroad only long enough to take on the veneer of Western education; it is a half-and-half knowledge; and it is these young men who become the discontented ones of China. When they return they do not find employment immediately, since they have grown out of touch with their country and their country's customs. They feel that they should begin at the top of the ladder, instead of working up slowly, rung by rung, as their fathers did before them. They must be masters all at once, not realizing that, even with their tiny grains of foreign knowledge, they have not yet experience to make them leaders of great enterprises or of men; yet they know too much to think of going back into their father's shop.

I realize that the students who go abroad from China have many difficulties to overcome. It is hard to receive their information and instruction in a language not their mother tongue. They have small chance to finish their education by practical work in bank or shop or factory. They get a mass of book knowledge and little opportunity to practice the theories they learn, and they do not understand that textbook knowledge is nearly all foreign to their country and to the temperament of their race. I often ask, when looking at my son, what is his gain? I presume it is in securing a newer, broader point of view, an ability to adjust himself to modern conditions, and a wider sympathy with the movements of the world.

China has for centuries been lost to the world by reason of her great exclusion, her self-satisfaction and blind reliance upon the ways marked out for her by sages of other days. These young men, with the West in their eyes, are coming back to shock their fathers' land into new channels. The process may not be pleasant for us of the old school, but quite likely it is necessary. Yet, I feel deep within me, as I look at them, that these new Westernized Easterners with their foreign ways and clever English are not to be the final saviors of China. They are but the clarion voices that are helping to awake the slumbering power. China must depend upon the firmer qualities of the common people, touched with the breath of the West. . . .

In no country is real learning held in higher esteem than in China. It is the greatest characteristic of the nation that, in every grade of society, education is considered above all else. Why, then, should our young people be ashamed of their country's learning? Instead of always quoting Byron, Burns, or Shelley, as do my son and daughter, let them repeat the beautiful words ot Tu Fu, Li Po, Po Chu-i, our poets of the golden age. The Chinese have devoted themselves to the cultivation of literature for a longer period by some thousands of years than any existing nation. The people who lived at the time of our ancestors, the peoples of Egypt, the Greeks, the Romans, have disappeared ages ago and have left only their histories writ in book or stone. The Chinese alone have continued to give the world their treasures of thought these five thousand years. To literature and to it alone they look for the rule to guide them in their conduct. To them all writing is most sacred. The very pens and papers used in the making of their books have become objects of veneration. Even our smallest village is provided with a scrap box into which every bit of paper containing words or printed matter is carefully placed, to await a suitable occasion when it may be reverently burned.

Change is now the order of the day, educationally as well as politically. We do not hear the children shouting their tasks at the top of their voices, nor do they learn by heart the thirteen classics, sitting on their hard benches within the simple rooms with earthen floor, where the faint light comes straggling through the unglazed windows on the boy who hopes to gain the prize that will lead him to the great Halls of Examination at Peking. If, while there, he is favored by the God of Learning and passes the examination, he will come back to his village an honor to his province, and all his world will come and do him reverence, from the viceroy in his official chair to the meanest worker in the fields. These old-time examinations are gone, the degrees that were our pride have been abolished, the subjects of study in the schools have been completely changed. The privileges that were once given our scholars, the social and political offices that were once open to the winner of the highest prize, have been thrown upon the altar of modernity. They say it is a most wise move and leads to the greater individualism, which is now the battle cry of China. The fault of the old examination, we are told, is the lack of original ideas that might be expressed by a student. He must give the usual interpretations of the classics. Now the introduction of free thought and private opinion has produced in China an upheaval in men's minds. The new scholars may say what they think wisest, and they even try to show that Confucius was at heart a staunch republican, and that Mencius only thinly veiled his sentiments of modern philosophy.

Perhaps the memory work of the Chinese education was wrong; but it served its purpose once, if tales are true.

It is said that many hundreds of years ago, the founder of the Chinese dynasty, the man of pride who styled himself Emperor the First, conceived the idea of destroying all literature that was before his reign, so he might be regarded by posterity as the founder of the Chinese Empire. It is believed by many Chinese scholars that this wicked thing was done, and that not a single perfect copy of any book escaped destruction. He even went so far as to bury alive five hundred of the best scholars of the land, that none might remain to write of this cruel deed. But the classics had been too well learned by the scholars, and were reproduced from memory to help form the minds of China for many tens of years. This could be done today if a similar tragedy were enacted. Thousands of boys have committed the great books to heart, and this storing in the mind of enormous books has developed in our race a marvelous memory, if, as others say, it has taken away their power of thinking for themselves.

Which is the best? Only time will tell. But we are told that the literati of China, the aristocracy of our land, must go. Yet, as of old, it is the educated men who will move China. Without them, nothing can be done, for the masses will respect education and the myriads will blindly follow a leader whom they feel to be a true scholar; and it will be hard to change the habits of a people who have been taught for centuries that education is another word for officialdom.

This new education, in my mind, must not be made so general; it must be made more personal. Three things should be taken into account: who the boy is, where he is, and where he is going. It is not meet to educate the son of my gatekeeper the same as my son. He should be a good workman, the best of his kind, better to fill the place to which the gods have called him. Give our boys the modern education, if we must, but remember and respect the lifework each may have to follow. Another thing we should remember: The progress in the boy's worldly knowledge should not free his intelligence without teaching him self-control. That is fatal for our Eastern race. Let him learn, in his books and in his laboratories, that he molds his destiny by his acts later in life, and thus gains true education, the education of the soul as well as of the mind.

I have written you a sermon, but it is a subject on which we mothers are thinking much. It is before us daily, brought to our

153

courtyards by our sons and daughters, and we see the good and the evil of trying to reach at a single bound the place at which other nations have at last arrived after centuries of weary climbing.

I must go to the women's quarters and stop their chattering. Oh, Mother of mine, why did you send to me that priest of yours?

Kwei-li

18

Dear Mother,

I must introduce you to your new daughter-in-law. Yes, I can see you start. I will tell you quickly. Your son has not taken to himself another wife, but it is I, Kwei-li, who should be made known to you anew. Kwei-li, the wife of the Governor of Kiang-su, who has become so foreignized that the mother of her husband would never know her. If things keep on the path they have gone for these last few moons, I fully expect you will see me with that band of women who are making such a great outcry for their rights and freedom. I cannot even explain them to you, as you would not understand.

My last adventure in the ways of the modern woman is in relation to the courtship of my son. Tang-si, my second son, is in love; and I, his mother, am aiding and abetting him, and allowing him to see his sweetheart in the foreign way. I know you will blush when you read this; but I have been in the hands of the gods and allowed not to speak of "custom," or propriety, and when I have tried to reason with my son and talk to him regarding what is seemly, he laughs at me and calls me pet names, and rubs my hair the wrong way and says I am his little mother. I knew that astounding fact years ago, and still I say that is no reason why I should go against all customs and traditions of my race.

I told him I was taught that men and women should not sit together in the same room, nor keep their wedding apparel in the same place, nor even cleanse them in the same utensils. They should not look upon each other, or hand a thing directly from man to woman. I was taught that it was seemly and showed a maidenly reserve to observe a certain distance in my relations even with my husband or my brothers, but I have found that the influence of reason upon love is like that of a raindrop upon the ocean, "one little mark upon the water's face and then it disappears."

Now I will tell you all about it. Tang-si came to me one day, and after speaking of many things of no importance, he finally said, "Mother, will you ask Kah-li, Wu Tai-tai's daughter, here to tea?" I said, "Why, is she a friend of your sister's?" He said, while looking down upon the floor, "I do not know, but—but—she is a special friend of mine." I looked at him in amazement. "You have seen her?" "Yes, many times. I want you to ask her to the house, where we may have a chance to talk." I sat back in my chair and looked at him, and said within myself, "Was ever a mother blessed with such children; what may I *next* expect?" He gave me a quick look, and came over and took my hand in his, and said, "Now, Mother, do not get excited, and don't look as if the Heavens were going to fall. I—well—you make it hard to tell you, but I want to marry Kah-li, and I would like a chance of seeing her as the foreign men see their wives before they marry them." I said, quite calmly for me, "You mean you are choosing your wife instead of allowing your father and mother to choose her?" He said, "Why, yes; I have to live with her and I ought to choose her." I said nothing—what is the use? I have learned that my menfolk have strong minds, which they certainly must have inherited from your honorable family. I said that first I would speak to her mother, and if she approved of her daughter's seeing my son in this most unbecoming manner, I would do whatsoever he wished in the matter. I could not wait, but went at once to the house of Wu Tai-tai. We discussed the matter over many cups of tea, and we saw that we are but clouds driven by the winds and we must obey.

She has been here for tea, and I am charmed with her. She is as pretty as a jewel of pure jade; I do not blame my son. She has laughter in her dancing eyes and seems as if she would sing away from year to year and see life always through the golden gleam of happy days. She is respectful and modest, and now I feel she is one of the family and I ask her to join us in all our feastings. She came to the feast when we burned the Kitchen God, and joined with us in prayers as he ascended to the great Spirit to tell him of our actions in the past year. I am afraid our young people do not believe much in this small God of the Household, who sits so quietly upon his shelf above the kitchen stove for twelve long months, watching all that goes on within the home, then gives his message for good or ill to Him above; but they are too respectful to say anything against it—in my hearing. They must respect the old gods until they find something better to take their place.

I do not know but that my son is right in this question of his courtship. It is pretty to see as they wander through the gardens, while we mothers sit upon the balconies and gossip. Their love seems to be as pure as spotless rice and "so long as color is color and life is life will the youth with his sublime folly wait for the meeting of his loved one." What matter if the winter days will come to them or if "the snow is always sure to blot out the garden"— today is spring, and love is love and youth is happy.

Your shameless daughter,
Kwei-li

1 9

My Dear Mother,

Your gifts, which came by the hand of Tuang-fang, are most welcome. We have already drunk the sun-dried tea, and it brings to thought the sight of the long, laden trays of the fragrant leaves as they lie in the sun on the mountainside. The rose wine we will use on occasions of special rejoicing; and I thank you again for the garments, which will bring comfort to so many in the coming days of cold. I was glad to see Tuang-fang, and sorry to hear that he, with his brother, are going so far away from home in search of labor. Is there not work enough for our men in the province without going to that land of heat and sickness? . . .

The more I come out from the courtyard and see our people, the more I admire them; I see the things that are so often lost sight of by those of other lands who seek to study them. They are a philosophical race and bear the most dreadful losses and calamities with wonderful bravery. Nothing daunts them. Behold the family of Tuang-fang: they saw their home ruined at the time of flood and began on the morrow to build on the remaining foundations. They saw their fields burned up by drought, and took their winter clothing to the pawnshop to get money to buy seed for the coming spring. They did not complain as long as they could get sufficient food to feed their bodies and the coarse blue cloth with which to clothe them, and when these failed they sent their three strong sons, the best of the family, to the rubber plantations of the south.

We hear so much in the papers here of the "Yellow Peril." If

there is a Yellow Peril, it lies in the fact that our men are ready to labor unceasingly for a wage on which most Europeans would starve, and on that pittance they manage to save and become rich and prosperous. They have gone into other lands wherever they have found an opening, and some of the southern countries, like Singapore and the Philippines, owe much of their commercial progress to our people. They are honest and industrious, and until the foreigner began to feel the pinch of competition, until he found that he must work all day and not sleep the hours away if he would be in the race with the man from the Eastern land, he had nothing to say about the character of the man from China. But as soon as he felt the pressure of want because of his sloth, he began to find that the "yellow man" was vicious, and soon his depravity became a by-word. The Chinese were abused because of their virtues rather than their vices, for things for which all other nations are applauded—love of work and economy. . . .

I think, hearing the gossip from your son's courtyard, that when China is again peaceful, there will be more chance for the men within her borders, who can then stay beside their fires and earn their food. Our land is a land of fertile soil, of rich minerals, and great rivers. It is said that there are millions and millions of acres on which food or other products can be grown, and that a great part of China may be made one vast garden. The German scientist who is trying to get a coal mine concession from the government told my husband that there were tens of millions of tons of coal of the best quality in China, and that the single province of Shansi could supply the entire world for thousands of years. No wonder the Germans are looking with longing eyes on China! But we want these riches and this labor for our people. If it is worth the time of men of other countries to come to this far-off land in search of what lies beneath our soil, it is worth our while to guard it and keep it for our own.

We hear the news of battles and of secret plottings, and I am worried about my son, who is in Canton, the province that seems to be the center of the rebellion and the breeding place of plots and treachery. I wonder what the outcome of it all will be; if after all this turmoil and bloodshed will China really become a different nation? It is hard to change the habits of a nation, and I think that China will not be changed by this convulsion. The real Chinese will be the same passive, quiet, slow-thinking, and slow-moving toiler, not knowing or caring whether his country is a republic or whether he is ruled by the Son of Heaven. These patient, plodding men of China have held together for countless thousands of years; and our government, even the government we are trying so hard to overturn and mold on Western lines, must have suited the country and the people, because nothing ever persists generation after generation, century after century, without being suited to its environment and more or less adapted to the changes that time always brings.

Confucius said, "When I was on a mission to Ch'u State, I saw a litter of young pigs nestling close to their dead mother. After a while they looked at her, then all left the dead body and went off. For their mother did not look at them anymore, nor did she seem anymore to be of their kind. What they loved was their mother: not the body that contained her, but that which made the body what it was."

That is the way of our country. She may leave the dead forms of her old government, perhaps it will be her misfortune to leave her religion, but the spirit of her government and the spirit of her religion she will always love.

K
w
e
i
.
l
i

But I must not gossip more with you over my dearly loved country and her people. I know I talk to you too much of politics and the greedy eyes of foreigners, which are fixed upon our land, but one cannot live in Shanghai, even behind the women's archway, without hearing, night and day, the things that move this, our world, so strongly. Even my small children play at war, shoot their rebels, build their fortresses, and drive the foreigners from off their piles of sand.

I cry to you, my Mother, because a heart must speak its bitterness, and here our lips are sealed to all. I dare not even tell your son, my husband, all that passes in my mind as I look from out my window at this fighting, struggling, maddened world that surges around me.

We are more troubled about our son.

Your daughter,
Kwei-li

20

My Dear Mother,

I send to you some silken wadding for the lining of your coat, also, a piece of sable to make a scarf for Su-su, and a box of clothing for her newborn son. The children each have written her a letter before Kwan-yin, to show our joy.

We have a guest, old General Wang, who is on his way to visit with my father. He is of the old, old China, and wags his head most dolefully over the troubles of his country, and says a republic will never succeed. My husband was bewailing the fact of the empty strongbox, and Wang said, "Why don't you do what I did when I was in command of the troops? When money was scarce, I simply stopped a dollar a month from each man's pay, and, lo, there was the money." He was quite shameless in regard to the old-time "squeeze" and said that it was necessary. When he was general he received the salary of an ill-paid servant and was expected to keep up the state of a small king. But there were many ways to fill the empty pockets. When a high official was sent to inspect his troops, men were compelled to come from the fields, the coolies to lay down their burdens, the beggar to leave his begging bowl, and all to stand straight as soldiers with guns within their hands. But when the officer was gone each went his way with a small present in his hand and did not appear again until the frightened official was compelled to sweep the highways and byways to find enough men to agree with his lists paid by the government.

But those times are past, and these old-time officials find it safer to retire to homes within their provinces.

He told us of Chung-tai, who was *Taotai* of our city at one time. Do you remember him? He made many millions in the exportation of rice at time of famine. He was asked to go to Peking, and promised a high position. He sent as answer the story of Chung Tzu the philosopher, who was fishing in the Piu when the Prince of Ch'u sent high officials to ask him to take charge of the state. Chung went on fishing and without turning his head said: "I have heard that in Ch'u there is a sacred tortoise that has been dead now some three thousand years, and that the prince keeps this tortoise carefully enclosed in a chest on the altar of the sacred temple. Now would this tortoise rather be dead and have its remains venerated, or be alive and wagging its tail in the mud?" "It would rather be alive and wagging its tail in the mud," said the officials. "Begone," said Chung. "The tortoise is a symbol of longevity and great wisdom. It would not befit me to aspire to greater wisdom than the tortoise. I too prefer the mud."

Chung spoke bravely in sending this reply to Peking; but no sooner was it sent than he gathered his family and his *cycee* and departed for Shanghai, where he feels more sure of the protection of the foreign settlements than he does of the kindly intentions of His Excellency Yuan toward his dollars.

The children have come home and are clamoring for their supper. They are growing rougher and noisier each day, and, I fear, are spending far too many hours in the servants' courtyard, where they hear of things not seemly for young ears. Can you send me Wong-si for a few months? She might be able to keep some order in my household, although I doubt a person of a nature not divine would be able to still the many tongues I have now about me.

We send you love, and greetings to your newborn great-grandson.

Kwei-li

My Dear Mother,

I have been in the country with my friend Ang Ti-ti. It was the time of pilgrimage to the graves of her family at the temple near Wu-seh. My household gave me many worries, and my husband said it was a time of rest for me, so we took a boat, with only a few servants, as I am tired of chattering women, and spent three long happy days amongst the hills. We sat upon the deck as the boat was slowly drawn along the canal, and watched the valley that autumn now is covering with her rare colors. All the green of the fields is changed. All the gay foliage of the trees upon the hillsides will soon be dead and crumbling. These withered leaves that once waved gaily in the air are lying now in clustered heaps, or fluttering softly to the ground like dull, brown butterflies who are tired with flight. The only touch of color is on the maple trees, which still cling with jealous hands to coverings of red and gold. The autumn winds wailed sadly around our cabin windows, and every gust brought desolation to tree and shrub and waving grass. Far away the setting sun turned golden trees to flame, and now and then on the sluggish waters of the canal would drift in lonely splendor a shining leaf that autumn winds had touched and made into a thing of more than beauty.

We anchored the first night by a marshy bank girdled with tall yellow reeds and dwarf bamboo, and from our quiet cabin listened to the rainy gusts that swept the valley. Out of the inky clouds the lightning flashed and lighted up each branch and stem and swaying

21

leaf, revealing to our half-blinded eyes the rain-swept valley; then darkness came with her thick mantle and covered all again.

We discussed the past, the present, and the future; and then, as always when mothers meet, the talk would turn to children. How moved we are by our children! We are like unto the Goddess of the Pine Tree. She came out from her rugged covering and bore a man-child for her husband's house, and then one day the overlord of all that land sent to cut down the pine tree, that its great trunk might form the rooftree of his temple. At the first blow of the axe the soul glided back into its hiding place, and the woman was no more. And when it fell, three hundred men could not move it from its place of falling; but her baby came and, putting out his hand, said, "Come," and it followed him quite quietly, gliding to the very doorway of the temple. So do our children lead us with their hands of love.

The second day we went to the temple to offer incense at the family shrine of An Ti-ti. We Chinese ladies love these pilgrimages to the shrines of our ancestors, and it is we who keep up the family worship. We believe that it is from the past that we must learn, and "the past is a pathway that spirits have trodden and made luminous." It is true, as Lafcadio Hearn has written, "We should be haunted by the dead men and women of our race, the ancestors that count in the making of our souls and have their silent say in every action, thought, and impulse of our life. Are not our ancestors in very truth our souls? . . .

"In this worship that we give the dead they are made divine. And the thought of this tender reverence will temper with consolation the melancholy that comes with age to all of us. Never in our China are the dead too quickly forgotten; by the simple faith they are still thought to dwell among their beloved, and their place within the home remains holy. When we pass to the land of shadows we know that loving lips will nightly murmur our names before the family shrine, that our faithful ones will beseech us in their pain and bless us in their joy. We will not be left alone upon the hillsides, but loving hands will place before our tablet the fruits and flowers and dainty food that we were wont to like, and will pour for us the fragrant cups of tea or amber rice wine.

"Strange changes are coming upon this land, old customs are vanishing, old beliefs are weakening, the thoughts of today will not be the thoughts of tomorrow; but of all of this we will know nothing. We dream that for us as for our mothers the little lamp will burn on through the generations; we see in fancy the yet unborn, the children, bowing their tiny heads and making the filial obeisance before the tablets that bear our family name."

This is our comfort, we who feel that "this world is not a place of rest, but where we may now take our little ease, until the landlord whom we never see, gives our apartment to another guest."

As I said to you, it is the women who are the preservers of the family worship and who are trying hard to cling to old loved customs. Perhaps it is because we suffer from lack of facility in adapting ourselves to new conditions. We are as fixed as the star in its orbit. Not so much the men of China but we women of the inner courtyards seem to our younger generation to stand like an immovable mountain in the pathway of their freedom from the old traditions.

In this course we are only following woman nature. An instinct more powerful than reason seems to tell us that we must preserve the thing we know. Change we fear. We see in the new ideas that our daughters bring from school, disturbers only of our life's ideals.

K
w
e
i
.
l
i

Yet the new thoughts are gathering about our retreats, beating at our doorways, creeping in at the closely shuttered windows, even winning our husbands and our children from our arms. The enclosing walls and the jealously guarded doors of our courtyards are impotent. While we stand a foe of this so-called progress, a guardian of what to us seems womanhood and modesty, the world around us is moving, feeling the impulse of a larger life, broadening its outlook and clothing itself in new expression that we hardly understand. We feel that we cannot keep up with this generation; and, seeing ourselves left behind with our dead gods, we cry out against the change that is coming to our daughters with the advent of this new education and the knowledge of the outside world. But—

All happy days must end, and we floated back to the busy life again. As we came down the canal in the soft moonlight it recalled those other nights to me upon the mountainside, and as I saw the lights of the city before us I remembered the old poem of Chang Chih Lo:

> The Lady Moon is my lover,
> My friends are the Oceans four,
> The Heavens have roofed me over,
> And the Dawn is my golden door.
> I would rather follow a condor,
> Or the sea gull soaring from ken,
> Than bury my Godhead yonder
> In the dust and whirl of men.

Your daughter,
Kwei-li

My Dear Mother,

I have not written you for many days. I came back from my happy country trip to find clouds of sorrow wrapping our home in close embrace. We hear Ting-fang is in deep trouble, and we cannot understand it. He is accused of being in league with the southern forces. Of course we do not believe it, my son is not a traitor; but black forebodings rise from deeps unknown, and the cold trail of fear creeps round my heart.

But I cannot brood upon my fears alone; this world seems full of sorrow. Just now I have stopped my letter to see a woman who was brought to the *Yamen* for trying to kill her baby daughter. She is alone, has no one to help her in her time of desolation, no rice for crying children, and nothing before her except to sell her daughter to the teahouse. She gave her sleep; and who can blame her?

Mother, send me all that you can spare from out of your plenty. I would I could give more. I would be a lamp for those who need a lamp, a bed for those who need a bed; but I am helpless. O, He who hears the wretched when they cry, deign to hear these mothers in their sorrow!

Your daughter,
Kwei-li

22

<table>
<tr><td>2 3</td></tr>
</table>

I know that you have heard the news, as it is in all the papers. Ting-fang is accused of throwing the bomb that killed General Chang. I write to reassure you that it cannot be true. I know my son. You know your family. No Liu could do so foul a deed.

Do not worry; we will send you all the news. The morrow's tidings will be well, so rest in peace.

Kwei-li

<table>
<tr><td>2 4</td></tr>
</table>

I thank you from my heart for the ten thousand *taels* telegraphed for the use of our son. Father has sent fifty thousand *taels* to be used in obtaining his freedom. I am sure it will not be needed, as my son is not the culprit. And if he were, it is not the olden time when a life could be bought for a few thousand ounces of silver, no matter how great the crime. We will not bribe the courts of law, even for our son.

But I am sure it will pass with the night's darkness, and we will wake to find it all a dream. I know, my mother's heart assures me, that my boy is innocent.

Do not speak or think of coming down. We will let you know at once all the news.

Kwei-li

[*Telegram*]
WE ARE LEAVING TONIGHT FOR CANTON.

We are entering Canton. The night denies me sleep, and my brain seems beating like the tireless shuttles upon a weaving loom. I cannot rest, but walk the deck till the moon fades from the dawn's pale sky, and the sun shines rose-colored against the morning's gray. Across the river a temple shines faintly through its ring of swaying bamboo, and the faint light glistens on the water dripping from the oars that bring the black-sailed junks with stores of vegetables for all that greedy city of living people. The mists cling lovingly to the hilltops, while leaves from giant banyan trees sway idly in the morning wind, and billows of smoke, like dull, gray spirits, roll upward and fade into a mist of clouded jade, touched with the golden fingers of the rising sun.

I see it all with eyes that do not see, because the creeping hours I count until I find my son.

2 6

Ting-fang has been tried and found guilty. The runners have brought me hour by hour the news; and even his father can see nothing that speaks in favor of his innocence. It is known and he confesses to having been with the men who are the plotters in this uprising. He was with the disloyal officers only a few hours before the bomb was thrown, but of the actual deed he insists that he knows nothing. All evidence points to his guilt. Even the official who sentenced him, a lifelong friend of ours, said in the open court that it hurt him sorely to condemn a man bearing the great name of Liu, because of what his father and his father's father had been to China, but in times such as these an example must be made; and all the world is now looking on to see what will be done.

I will write to you and telegraph you further news; I can say no more at the present; my heart is breaking.

Kwei-li

A man came to us secretly last night and offered to effect my son's escape for fifty thousand *taels*. He said that arrangements could be made to get him out of the country—and we have refused! We told him we could give no answer until the morning, and I walked the floor the long night through, trying to find the just pathway.

We cannot do it. China is at the parting of the ways; and if we, her first officials, who are taking the stand upon the side of justice and new ideas of honor, do not remain firm in hours of great temptation, what lesson have we to give to them who follow where we lead? It must not be said that our first acts were those of bribery and corruption. If my son is a traitor, we must let him pay. He must give his life upon the altar of the new China. We cannot buy his life. We are of the house of Liu, and our name must stand, so that, through the years to come, it will inspire those who follow us to live and die for China, the country that we love.

27

28

My Mother,

From the red dawn until the dense night fell, and all the hours of darkness through, have my weary feet stumbled on in hopeless misery, waiting, listening for the guns that will tell to me that my son is gone. At sunset a whispered message of hope was brought, then vanished again, and I have walked the lengthened reach of the great courtyard, watching as, one by one, the lanterns die and the world is turning into gray. Far away toward the rice fields the circling gulls rise, flight on flight, and hover in the blue, then fly away to life and happiness in the great world beyond. In the distance, faint blue smoke curls from a thousand dwellings of people who are rising and will greet their sons, while mine lies dead. Oh, I thought that tears were human only, yet I see each blade of shining grass weighed down with dewdrop tears that glimmer in the air. Even the grass would seem all sorrow-filled as my heart.

The whole night through the only sound has been the long-drawn note of the bamboo flute, as the seller passes by, and the wind that wailed and whistled and seemed to bring with it spirits of the other world who came and taunted me that I did not save my son. Why, *why* did I not save him! What is honor, what is this country, what is our fame, in comparison to his dear life? Why did we not accept the offer of escape! It was ours to give or take; we gave, and I repent—O God, *how I repent*! My boy, my boy! I will be looking for his face in all my dreams and find despair.

Do you remember how he came to me in answer to the Towers of
Prayer I raised when my firstborn slept so deep a sleep he could not
be awakened even by the voice of his mother? But that sorrow
passed and I rose to meet a face whose name is memory. At last I
knew it was not kindness to mourn so for my dead. Over the River
of Tears is their silent road, and when mothers weep too long, the
flood of that river rises, and their souls cannot pass but must wander to and fro. But to those whom they leave with empty arms they
are never utterly gone. They sleep in the darkest cells of tired hearts
and busy brains, to come at echo of a voice that recalls the past.

My sleeve is wet with bitter rain; but tears cannot blot out the
dream visions that memory wakes, and the dead years answer to my
call. I see my boy, my baby, who was the gift of kindly gods. When
I first opened my eyes upon him, I closed them to all the world besides, and my soul rested in peace beside the jewel within its cradle.
The one sole wish of my heart was to be near him, to sit close by
his side, to have him day by day within my happy sight, and to lay
my cheek upon his rose-tipped feet at night. The sun's light seemed
more beautiful where it touched him, and the moon that lit my
Heaven was his eyes.

As he grew older he was fond of asking questions to which none
but the gods could give reply, and I answered as only mothers will.
When he wished to play I laid aside my work to play with him, and
when he tired and wished to rest, I told him stories of the past. At
evening when the lamps were lighted I taught him the words of the

evening prayer, and when he slept I brought my work close by his cradle and watched the still sweetness of his face. Sometimes he would smile in his dreams, and I knew that Kwan-yin the Divine was playing shadow-play with him, and I would murmur a silent prayer to the Mother of all Mercies to protect my treasure and keep him from harm.

      ◊   ◊   ◊

I can see my courtyard in far Szechwan; and in the wooden box within my bedroom are all his baby clothes. There are the shoes with worn-out toes and heels that tried so hard to confine restless, eager feet; the cap with Buddha and his saints, all broken and tarnished where tiny baby teeth have left their marks; and, Mother, do you remember when we made him clothing like the soldier at the *Yamen*? And the bamboo that the gateman polished he carried for a gun . . .

O my son, my son! How can I rise to begin the bitter work of life through the twilights yet to come!

How can I tell you, Mother of mine, of the happiness within my heart! It is passed; it was but a dream, a mirage. He is here, my boy, his hand in mine, his cheek against my cheek; he is mine own again, my boy, by man-child, my son.

It was not he; the culprit has been found; and in the golden morning light my son stood free before me. I cannot write you more at present, I am so filled with joy. What matter if the sun shines on wrinkles and white hair, the symbol of the fullness of my sorrow—I have mine own again!

My Dear Mother,

I can talk to you more calmly, and I know you hunger for full news. Do you remember Liang Tai-tai, she who I wrote you was so anxious for the mercy of the gods that she spent her time praying instead of looking after her household duties and her son? He was the one who tried to pass the Dark Water and I talked to him and we sent him to the Prefect at Canton. It was he who found the man for whom my son was accused. It seemed he felt he owed us much for helping him in his time of trouble, and now he has repaid.

I feel that I have laughed too oft at Liang Tai-tai and her gods, but now I will go with her from temple shrine to temple shrine. I will buy candles, incense, spirit money for her, until the gods look down in wonder from their thrones. I am so filled with gratitude that when I see my friend, I will fall before her feet and bathe them with my happy tears for having trod the path of motherhood and given to the world a man-child, who has saved for me my son.

Kwei-li

31

My Mother,

We are home, and have not written you for long, but have telegraphed you twice daily, so that you have been assured that all is well.

We found our dear one, Li-ti, bending over her babe, holding it safely, nestling it, murmuring, softly, whispers of mother love. This son, born in the hour of trouble and despair, is a token of the happiness to come, of the new life that will come forth from grief and sorrow.

He has learned a lesson, this boy of mine, and he will walk more carefully, guard more surely his footsteps, now he is the father of a son.

Kwei-li

O Mother of graciousness, we are coming to you! When all the hills are white with blossoms, we shall set forth, our eager hearts and souls one great, glad longing for the sight of you standing in the archway, searching with earnest gaze the road, listening for the bearers' footsteps as we mount the hillside.

We leave this place full of trial and turmoil. I want my children to come within the shelter of your compound walls, where safety lies; and with the "shell of forgetfulness" clasped tightly in our hands, we will forget these days of anguish and despair. Then only, when my dear ones are far from here, shall my soul obtain the peace it craves, forgetful of the hostile, striving, plotting treachery of this foreign world I fear.

We are coming home to you, Mother of my husband, and I have learned in life's great, bitter school that the joy of my Chinese womanhood is to stand within the sheltered courtyard, with my family close about me, and my son's son in my arms.

Kwei-li

金

蓮